D0886710

EURASIAN FOLK AND FAIRY TALES

Eurasian
Folk and Fairy Tales

by I. F. Bulatkin

illustrated by Howard Simon

Criterion
New York

CONTENTS

THE THREE GOLDEN HAIRS OF GRANDDAD SOL
A Russian Tale   9

THE GOLDEN PITCHER
A Mongolian Tale   22

THE WISE WIFE
A Russian Tale   27

A RUPEE EARNED
An Armenian Tale   39

STRETCH, PUFF AND BLAZER
A Russian Tale   44

THE RICH LANDOWNER AND HIS WORKER
An Armenian Tale   57

MOLLA NASREDDIN AND HIS DONKEY
A Persian Tale   64

THE PEDDLER AND HIS MONKEYS
An Indian Tale   69

THE GOLDEN DOLLS
An Indian Tale   71

THE PEASANT AND THE TSAR
A Russian Tale   75

THE HARE AND THE TIGER
An Afghanistan Tale   80

THE MATCH-MAKING OF A
MOUSE
A Japanese Tale   82

THE NIGHTINGALE AND THE KHAN
A Tartar Tale   85

THE GOAT
An Armenian Tale   90

THE PEASANT AND THE BARON
A Russian Tale   95

TWO RASCALS
A Kalmuk Tale   98

NABOOKIN
An Iranian Tale   103

SHAYDOOLA
A Tale of Azerbaijan   106

THE BAT'S CHOICE
An Indian Tale   111

KNOWLEDGE AND LUCK
A Czech Tale   114

THE SPRING AY-PETRI
A Legend of Crimea   120

A POOR PEASANT AND TWO NOBLES
A Tartar Tale   123

THE WISE DOCTOR
                                                          124

THE SHREWD PEASANT
A Russian Tale   125

TO EVA, NINA, TAMARA
AND ELIZABETH

THE THREE GOLDEN HAIRS
OF GRANDDAD SOL
A Russian Tale

There once lived a king who enjoyed hunting wild animals deep in the forest. While chasing a deer one day, the king lost his way. He always hunted alone, so he was overjoyed when, at dusk, he saw a cabin by a clearing in the forest. Here lived a charcoal peddler. The king offered him a rich reward if the peddler would show him the way out of the forest.

"I would be very happy to help you," said the charcoal peddler, "but my wife is about to give birth. I can't leave her alone. Besides, how can you travel during the night? It would be best if you slept in the loft and tomorrow I will show you to the main road."

That night a son was born to the charcoal peddler's wife. The king lay in the loft above but was unable to sleep.

At midnight a light flickered in the room below. The king peeped though the crack in the ceiling. The peddler

was asleep and his wife lay exhausted by his side. Around the baby stood three old women dressed in white, each holding a lighted candle.

The first said: "I foresee that this child will meet great dangers during his lifetime."

The second said: "I foresee that he will overcome all the dangers and have a long life."

The third said: "I foresee that he will marry the daughter, born this day, of the king who sleeps in the loft."

The old women then blew out their candles. There was silence once more.

The king suddenly felt a lump in his throat. He could not sleep the rest of the night. All his thoughts were centered on how to forestall the prophecy he had just heard. When morning came the baby started to cry. The charcoal peddler arose to find that his wife would never awake from her sleep.

"My poor little orphan, he began to sob. "What am I to do with him now?"

"Give me your baby," said the king. "I will see that he is well taken care of. In return you will be given enough money so that you need never work in your lifetime."

The charcoal peddler agreed. The king promised to send someone for the baby. When he returned to his castle he was delighted to hear he was the father of a beautiful daughter, born the very night he had spied on the three sorceresses. The king then became concerned and sent for his trusted servant.

"Follow this path through the forest and you will find

the charcoal peddler's hut. Give him this money; he will give you a baby, which you are to drown before you arrive home. If you do not obey my command you will be severely punished."

The servant left, found the hut, took the child and placed him in a basket. When he came to a bridge across a wide and deep river, he tossed the basket with the child into the water.

"Farewell, unwanted son-in-law," said the king when the servant returned to the castle.

The king believed the baby had been drowned, but in this he was mistaken. The basket drifted down the river like a canoe and the child did not wake. Finally the basket floated by the hut of a fisherman, who sat mending his nets on the bank of the river. He saw the basket, jumped into his boat, and brought the basket and baby to his wife.

"You always wanted a son. Well, the river brought us this child."

The fisherman's wife was delighted, and she looked after the baby as if he was her very own. They named him Sailor because he had come to them by way of the river.

The river flowed peacefully on, and the years passed swiftly. The child grew up to be a handsome boy. He was so handsome, in fact, that none could compare with him.

One summer day the king rode by the fisherman's hut. It was warm, and the king stopped for a drink of water. When Sailor gave him the water, the king so admired the lad that he said:

"You have a fine-looking boy, fisherman. Is he your son?"

"No," replied the fisherman. "Exactly twenty years ago I found him floating down the river in a little basket. He has been our child ever since."

The king's eyes grew dim. He turned as white as a sheet. For this was the child he had ordered to be drowned. However, he soon regained control, alighted from his horse, and said:

"I need someone to send to the castle, but as you see I have no attendant with me. Is it possible to send this lad?"

"Your royal majesty need only ask and the boy will gladly go," answered the fisherman.

The king sat down and wrote a note to his queen:

"The lad with this message must be put to death at once. He is my terrible enemy. See that this is done before I return home. Such is my command."

Having folded the note, the king placed his seal on it with his ring.

Sailor set out at once to deliver the message. He traveled through the dense forest, strayed off his course, and soon lost his way. He wandered among the trees until darkness, when he met an old woman.

"Where does your journey take you, Sailor?" she asked.

"I was carrying a message to the king's palace but strayed off the path. Can you tell me how to find the main road, Granny?"

"You cannot travel in the dark," answered the old woman. "Come, stay with me for the night. You won't be a stranger, as I am your godmother."

The youth agreed and they went only a short distance when suddenly before them a beautiful house appeared.

Here he spent the night. While he slept, the old woman took the message from his pocket and replaced it with another which read:

"This lad is being sent by me. He should be immediately married to our daughter. I have chosen him for our son-in-law. Do this before my return. Such is my order."

When the queen read the message she arranged for the marriage at once. The princess and the queen so admired the lad that they could hardly take their eyes off him. For the princess and Sailor it was love at first sight.

In a few days the king returned to the castle. When he heard what had happened he became very angry with his wife.

"But you ordered this marriage yourself before your return," replied the queen, and she showed him the message.

The king took the message, examined the seal, the writing, and the paper, and saw that all was genuine.

He called for his son-in-law and questioned him about what had happened on his way to the castle.

Sailor told how he had traveled through the forest, how he had lost his way and stayed overnight with his godmother.

"What did she look like?"

So Sailor described the old woman.

Now the king realized that this was the same crone who twenty years ago prophesied that his daughter would marry the charcoal peddler's son. He thought and thought, and then he said:

"What has been done cannot be undone. However, you

can't be my son-in-law without some deed to prove your-self. If you want to be a husband to my daughter, then as a gift to me you must obtain three golden hairs from Granddad Sol.

The king thought that this was the way to rid himself of his unwanted son-in-law.

Sailor bade good-by to his beloved princess and de-parted on his quest.

Because his godmother was a sorceress it was not very hard for him to find the way. He traveled over hills, dales, and across oceans until he came to a blue sea. He saw a boat with a ferryman.

"Can you please help me, old ferryman?"

"That I can, my young traveler. Where are you going?"

"To Granddad Sol in search of the three golden hairs."

"Indeed! I have long waited for such a messenger. For twenty years I have been ferrying people and no one has come to replace me. If you promise to ask Granddad Sol when my work here will be done, I'll take you across."

Sailor promised and was ferried across the blue sea.

In time he came to a large town, which was very old and poor. In the town he met an old man leaning on a cane, who could hardly drag himself along on his feeble legs.

"Can you please help me, Granddad?"

"Perhaps, young man. Where are you going?"

"To Granddad Sol to find the three golden hairs."

"Oh! Ah! We have long waited for such a messenger. I must take you to our king at once."

They came before the king, who said:

"I understand that you are a messenger to Granddad

Sol. We once had an apple tree that bore youth-giving fruit. If anyone ate an apple, even if he was near death, he would become young again. It has been twenty years since the apple tree bore fruit. If you see Granddad Sol ask him how we can be helped in this matter. You will be well rewarded for learning the answer."

Sailor promised to help, and the king wished him well.

Later he came to another town which was half in ruins. Not far away a son was burying his father. Tears the size of peas rolled down his cheeks.

"Can I help you, sad mourner?" inquired Sailor.

"Thank you, distant traveler. Where are you going?"

"I am on my way to Granddad Sol in search of the three golden hairs."

"To Granddad Sol! It is sad that you did not arrive sooner. Our king has long awaited such a messenger. I must take you to him at once."

They arrived before the king, who said:

"I hear that you are a messenger to Granddad Sol. We once had a spring with life-giving waters. If a sick person drank some of the water he would be well again. This water, sprinkled on the dead, would bring him back to life. Yes, it is already twenty years since we had this water. If you promise to ask Granddad Sol how our problem can be solved, I will reward you."

Sailor promised to do this, and the king wished him well.

Sailor continued his travels deep within a pine forest. In the heart of this forest he came to a large green meadow filled with beautiful flowers. In this meadow was a golden castle, and this castle belonged to Granddad Sol. It shone like a blazing flame. Sailor entered the castle and at first he saw no one, then in a corner he noticed an old woman spinning.

"Welcome, Sailor," she greeted him. "I am happy to see you."

This was the godmother at whose home he had stayed when he was lost in the forest.

"Why did you come here?"

"The king will not have me for a son-in-law without some gift, so he sent me off in search of three golden hairs from Granddad Sol."

The old woman smiled and said:

"Granddad Sol, the bright sun, is my son. In the morning he is a youth, at midday a man, in the evening he is an old man. I will see that you receive the three golden hairs from his head to prove that I really am your godmother. But my son must not see you. Although he has a kind heart, when he returns home hungry in the evening it could easily happen that if he found you, he would eat you for his supper. Get into this tub where I will hide you."

Sailor told her to ask Granddad Sol the three questions to which he had promised answers.

"I'll ask him," she replied. "But you must listen and remember what he says."

Suddenly there was a rush of wind from the outside, and through the westerly window there entered the sun—an old man with golden hair.

"I smell a man," he said. "Who is here with you, mother?"

"Now who could be here that you could not see, star

of day? Simply because you travel across the earth all day where you smell people, it is not too suprising that when you return in the evening you still think you smell a man."

The old man made no reply to this but sat down to eat. Afterward he placed his golden head on his mother's lap and fell asleep. When she saw that he was asleep, she pulled out a golden hair and let it fall to the floor. He arose like a lion.

"What do you want, Mother?" he asked.

"Nothing, my son. I dozed off and had a terrible dream."

"What was this dream?"

"I saw a town which had a spring of living waters. If one drank this water he would become well. If a person died and the water was sprinkled on him, he would become alive again. But it has been twenty years since the waters of this spring last flowed. What is necessary to make the waters of this spring flow again?"

"This is simple, Mother. At the bottom of the spring sits a frog who does not let the water flow. If the frog is killed and the spring is cleaned, the waters will flow again."

The old man again fell asleep. The old woman pulled a second golden hair from his head and let it fall to the floor.

"What is wrong with you, Mother?"

"Nothing, my son, nothing. I fell asleep and again had a terrible dream. In a certain town there was once a wonderful apple tree that bore youth-giving fruit. If one became old and ate this fruit, he would become young again. It is now twenty years since the apple tree last bore fruit. What can be done?"

"This problem is easily solved. Under the apple tree lives a snake that sucks the juices of the tree. If the snake is slain and the tree transplanted, it will again bear fruit."

The old man fell asleep a third time. The old woman pulled out the third golden hair.

"Why don't you let me sleep, Mother?" he shouted, and was about to get up.

"Sleep, my son, sleep. Do not get angry. I did not awake you on purpose. I fell asleep and had a strange dream. In my dream I saw a ferryman on the blue sea. He has worked twenty years on this job and no one comes to replace him. When will he be free of his work?"

"It seems that his mother did not teach him well," said the old man. "Let him give the oars to someone else and then jump ashore. This other person will become the ferryman. Now please let me sleep in peace. I have to arise early this morning to dry the tears of the princess. She has cried all night because her husband, the son of the charcoal peddler, was sent by the king for three of my golden hairs."

At daybreak there was again a great gust of wind. On the lap of the old woman sat a beautiful golden-haired child—the blazing sun. He said good-by to his mother and went out of the castle through the east window.

The old woman got Sailor out of the tub and said, "Here are the three golden hairs. You heard what Granddad Sol said in reply to your three questions. You can depart now. You will never see me again."

When Sailor arrived at the first town the king asked if there was any good news.

"Good news," answered Sailor. "Give orders to have the spring cleaned and kill the frog which sits at the bottom of the spring. The waters will start to flow."

The king ordered this to be done at once, and when he saw the spring flow as before, Sailor was given twelve horses, white as swans, and as much gold, silver, and precious stones as he could carry away.

When he arrived at the second town, Sailor was asked by the king what news he brought.

"Good news," answered Sailor. "Order the apple tree to be dug up. There you will find a snake beneath the roots. Kill this snake and replant the apple tree and it will again bear fruit."

At once the king ordered this to be done and the apple tree blossomed overnight as if someone had heaped roses upon it. The king was overjoyed and he gave Sailor twelve horses, black as ravens, and all the riches he could carry.

Sailor continued his journey until he came to the blue sea. The ferryman asked if the answer to his problem has been found.

"I have the answer," said Sailor. "Ferry me across first and I will tell you."

The ferryman was stubborn but knew there was nothing else he could do. He ferried Sailor across the blue sea with all the horses and riches.

"When you ferry the next person," said Sailor, "give the oars to him and jump ashore. This person will then become the ferryman. . . ."

The king could not believe his eyes when Sailor placed

before him the three golden hairs of Granddad Sol. The princess wept for joy because Sailor had returned.

"Where did you get the beautiful horses and so much wealth?" asked the king.

"I earned all of this," replied Sailor. He then told how he helped one king with his youth-restoring apple tree which made the old young again. He also told about the living waters that made the sick well and brought the dead to life.

"Youth-giving apples! Living waters!" repeated the king. "If I could eat such apples, I would be young again. And if I should die these waters would give me new life."

The king did not wait but set out at once to find the youth-giving apple tree and the living waters. And he has not been heard from since. The son of a charcoal peddler remained the husband of the princess, just as the sorceress had foretold.

As for the king, for all we know he may still be ferrying travelers across the deep blue sea.

THE GOLDEN PITCHER
A Mongolian Tale

There once lived a sly and cruel king. Not a single man did he pity, nor was there a thing he revered. Rich and poor feared this king, whereas he feared but one thing—old age. All day long he would stare at himself in a mirror. If he spied a gray hair, he would color it with dye. If he discovered a little wrinkle, he would smooth it out with his fingers.

"I must not grow old," he said to himself. "Now I am feared by all, but if I become weak and decrepit, my people will no longer obey me."

So to banish old age from his realm, the king commanded that every old man be slain. A man's hair had but to turn gray and that was the end of him.

From all parts of the land women and children, young men and maidens came bearing rich presents for the king. They implored him to have mercy.

Finally the king became bored with hearing so many complaints and lamentations. He summoned his heralds and commanded them to go to all the cities and villages and proclaim his mercy.

The heralds saddled their horses and set out in all directions, sounding their trumpets at the crossroads and market places, crying:

"Take heed, everybody! Listen, everybody! The king proclaims his mercy. Whosoever will bring up the gold pitcher from the bottom of the lake will save his father's head and receive the pitcher as a prize. Such is the king's mercy! But whosoever tries to bring up the pitcher and fails will not save his father's head and will lose his own as well. Such is the king's mercy!"

The heralds hadn't got around half the country before brave youths began to meet and assemble at the lake. The bank of the lake was steep, and from its height through the crystal water gleamed the outline of the golden pitcher. It had a slender neck, an engraved design, and bowed handles.

Ninety-nine brave youths tried their luck on the bank of the lake, and the cruel king chopped off ninety-nine heads, for none could bring up the pitcher from the lake.

Now at this time there lived in the land a youth named Ozmin, who dearly loved his father. When he saw that age was creeping up on the old man, that wrinkles were appearing on his face, that his hair was becoming grizzled and hoary, Ozmin led his father far away into the mountains.

Every day when the sun set behind the mountains the youth would slip through a gorge and bring food to his father. One day, as Ozmin sat beside his father, he felt sad.

"What trouble have you in your heart, my son?" asked the old man. "Perhaps it is tiresome for you to come here every day?"

"No, Father," answered the youth; "to see you well and unharmed I would come to these mountains three times a day. I have another trouble. The king's pitcher won't leave my mind day or night. I think about it and think about it. I can't understand why it is that when you look from the bank into the water, you can see the pitcher so clearly that it seems you can bring it up with your hand and it will be yours. But if someone jumps into the lake, the water at once becomes muddy and the pitcher sinks to the bottom."

The old man was thoughtful.

"Tell me, my son," he asked finally, "is there not on the bank, in that place from where the pitcher is seen, some kind of tree?"

"Yes, Father," the youth replied, "on the bank there stands a big spreading tree."

"But do you remember well," asked the old man, "if the pitcher can be seen in the tree's shadow?"

"Yes, Father," said the youth, "a broad shadow from the tree extends over the water and the pitcher shines out in the shadow."

"Well, then, listen to me, my son," said the old man. "Climb up into that tree and you will find the king's pitcher in the branches. The pitcher in the water—that is merely a reflection."

As swift as an arrow, the youth sped to the king.

"I pledge my head," he cried. "I will bring up your pitcher, merciful king!"

The king laughed. "Your head alone is all I need for a good round number. I have already cut off ninety-nine. Yours will be the hundredth."

"That may be so," replied the youth. "Yet may it also

be that by just this head your ciphers will never be round."

"Well, try your luck," said the king; and he ordered his servant to sharpen the blade of his ax.

Ozmin hastened to the lake and without hesitation climbed the tree that grew on the bank. The people gathered around and groaned in dismay.

"The gods will pardon him. Truly he has lost his common sense from terror," they said. "Perhaps he wants to jump from the tree," said others.

But the youth climbed to the very top of the tree, and there in the midst of its branches he found the golden pitcher with the slender neck, the engraved design, and the bowed handles. It hung from the tree upside down so that it seemed to be standing in the water. Thus he found it . . . upside down on its neck. He snatched it from the tree and took it to the king.

The king threw up his hands. "Well," he said, "I did not expect such wisdom from you. Is it possible that you, by yourself, guessed how to obtain the pitcher?"

"No," said Ozmin. "I did not conceive this thing myself. But I have an aged father, whom I have concealed from your gracious eye. It was he who foresaw where the pitcher was hidden.'

The king thought a while. "Apparently old men are wise," he said. "What a hundred youths could not guess, one old man divined!"

From this time forth in that country no one dared lay a finger on an old man. Wisdom and gray hair were respected by all. When the young people met an old man on the highway, they made way for him and bowed low.

THE WISE WIFE
A Russian Tale

Once upon a time a tsar's son went hunting. While chasing a deer he became lost in the forest. The tsarevich halted his horse and wondered how he could reach the main road. He searched all through the night but could find neither a path nor a road leading out of the forest.

At dawn the tsarevich and his horse were exhausted and they were still deep in the forest. However, with more light the tsarevich found a narrow path which he followed until he came to a broad meadow; and just beyond was a village. He rode into the village and stopped at the first cottage which had smoke rising from its chimney.

"Since the fire is lit," he said to himself, "the mistress of the house must be awake."

Dismounting, he climbed the porch stairs and came to the door. The door was ajar, and he heard a maiden's voice from behind the stove:

"It is too bad when the courtyard lacks a voice and the cottage has no eyes. Stay where you are, young man."

The tsarevich thought: What is this she is saying? Is she out of her mind? Then he asked:

"Do you live here alone or with your parents?"

"Why should I live alone?" said the girl from behind the stove. "I live here with my father, mother and brother, but they are not home today."

"Where are they?" asked the young visitor.

"My parents left to exchange their sorrows while my brother left to venture a hundred rubles in the hope of gaining five rubles."

Again the tsar's son could make neither head nor tail of her reply.

When the maiden stepped out from behind the stove the tsarevich took one look at the girl and he was stricken as though with paralysis. He stood like a tree stump, unable to talk or move. She was so beautiful one could travel the whole world over and not find another like her. Her braided hair hung down to her waist and was the color of daffodils; her blue eyes were like two bright stars; and her cheeks were the color of red poppies. She was like a rare morning in May.

The lovely girl spoke pleasantly to the tsarevich:

"Please come in and rest. Tell me your name and what brings you here."

The tsarevich recovered enough to sit on a bench. He told her how he had lost his way in the forest and then had come to the village.

"What did you say about a yard without a voice and a cottage without eyes? I did not understand a thing."

The girl smiled. "What is so difficult to understand? If we had a dog in the yard, he would have barked at you. I would have heard him and known a stranger was approaching. That is what a yard without a voice means.

And a cottage without eyes means that if there were children in the house, they would have seen a stranger through the window and told me."

"Now explain to me about your parents and your brother," the young man pleaded.

Oh, what a slow-witted but handsome young man this is, thought the girl, and then replied:

"My parents have gone to a wake to mourn a departed friend. When their time comes and they pass on, then their good friends will come to mourn for them. My brother rode away on his hundred-ruble horse to hunt rabbits. Possibly he will catch a rabbit, a gain of about five rubles. But if his horse is harmed, he stands to lose one hundred rubles."

She prepared food while they talked.

"Please sit down and have some breakfast. You are welcome to whatever there is."

After serving food and tea she told him how to find his way back, assuring him that if he followed her directions he would be home by evening.

The tsar's son rode away, and from that moment he was a changed person. At home he did not eat or drink because his thoughts were always of the beautiful maiden.

His parents became deeply concerned about their son's unhappiness. They arranged great banquets but the tsarevich remained downcast.

"He should get married," said the tsar. "When he has his own family all of his sadness will disappear like magic."

The tsar called his son.

"We have decided, beloved son, that the time has come for you to marry. You are now of age and it would gladden our hearts to see grandchildren. A bride should not be difficult to find. Any princess or tsarevna would be happy to be your wife."

"In our land there is a maiden of great beauty," replied the tsarevich.

"Very good," said the tsar. "Tell me where to send the match-makers. In what village did you meet this royal maiden?"

The tsarevich told how he had gone hunting and come upon an unfamiliar village. Here in this strange village he had met the girl whose beauty had left him breathless.

"She is not a tsarevna nor a princess," he told his father. "I love a peasant's daughter and will have no one else for my bride."

The tsar threw up his hands in horror.

"I will never accept a peasant's daughter into my family."

"That is your choice, Father. But as for me, I will never marry if I can't have her," the son answered.

He begged to be excused and left the room.

The tsar tried vainly to reach a just solution.

"My son will obey me now but when I die and he becomes tsar then he will surely marry this peasant girl."

The tsar told his wife about the peasant girl and the tsarvena began to weep.

"Oh, what a terrible thing. What are we to do now?"

"I have reached a decision," her husband said. "Have the servant call the tsarevich."

"We have given this matter much thought and have come to an agreement," said the tsar to his son. "If the

30

maiden you love is able to complete three of the tasks I set before her, then you may marry her. However, if she fails she will lose her life."

He gave his son a stalk of flax.

"Give her this stalk of flax. Have her spin it into yarn and make me a shirt."

The tsarevich rode off saddened by his father's command.

From her window the maiden saw the tsarevich approaching and she ran out to meet him. At the gate they exchanged many fond greetings.

"Have you returned with good tidings?" she asked.

The tsarevich could say nothing but stood first on one foot and then on the other. At last he blurted out:

"I have fallen in love with you. Will you marry me?"

She tried to hide the blushes on her face. Finally she replied in a whisper:

"I love you too. My parents will consent to our marriage, but you must ask your parents."

The tsarevich told her all that had happened and gave her the flaxen stalk.

When she heard the request of the tsar she smiled. She then broke a twig from a birch broom.

"Let the tsar make me a spinning wheel and a spindle from this twig so that I can loom the finest linen. I will then complete his task."

The tsarevich rode home and gave the birch twig to his father with the maiden's request.

"Well, you are a clever one, but I am more clever."

The tsar ordered that a hundred hard-boiled eggs be

prepared. He told his son to take the eggs to his bride. From these eggs she must raise chickens which would be served at their wedding feast.

Hearing of this new task, the tsarevich again became saddened. He dared not complain but rode off to his bride.

The maiden took the eggs. She then made a pot of millet porridge and said:

"Give this porridge to your father. He is to plant the millet and raise it until it is full grown. Otherwise the chickens will have nothing to eat."

The tsarevich returned home with the millet porridge for his father.

The tsar listened to the maiden's message and told his son to return in three days.

The old tsar thought and thought, and on the third morning laughed merrily.

"Only now will that peasant woman know what it is to deal with a tsar!"

He called his son.

"Go forth and invite your bride as our guest. It is necessary for us to get acquainted before the wedding. Have her come to us neither dressed nor undressed; she should not offer a gift and yet not come without one; she should not walk alone or come on horseback, but is to be led."

The tsarevich went to his bride and told her of the tsar's difficult request. Her mother, father and brother became most unhappy.

"Oh, how could the tsar ask such an impossible task."

But the beautiful maiden replied happily:

"Tell your parents to expect me tomorrow afternoon."

The tsarevich rode away.

She then told her brother:

"Catch me a live rabbit and a live quail for tomorrow."

The brother at once left for the forest.

The girl comforted her parents. "Please do not be sad. Everything will be done as the tsar asked."

The next day, just before noon, the tsar sat in his upper chambers looking from his window. He saw the maiden approaching and issued orders that when the gates were opened to admit the girl to the palace grounds, ferocious dogs were to be released from their chains.

He laughed as he muttered:

"Too bad, young maiden, you had to live to this day when the dogs will tear you to pieces."

As he watched from his window the girl came nearer and nearer. Instead of clothes she was draped in layers of net so that she was neither dressed nor undressed. She led a rabbit by a pair of reins and chased it with a stick, as she approached neither walking alone nor on horseback, yet was being led. Just as the gates opened, the ferocious dogs were released.

The tsar saw all this from his window, but as he came down to the veranda the dogs were already far in the distance chasing the rabbit. The veranda steps creaked. The tsar turned to see the maiden climbing the stairs. She was draped in layers of fine mesh net. Even dressed as she was, no words, spoken or written, could begin to describe her beauty.

The maiden curtsied, smiled at the tsar, and said:

"It is a great honor to be invited by the tsar and to have him meet me on the veranda." She extended her hands. "Please accept my gift."

The tsar reached for the gift as the maiden released it. Instantly, the quail flew under the very nose of the tsar and then rose into the clear blue sky.

The tsar scratched his beard as he watched the bird fly away.

"Not with a gift and yet not without a gift," said the maiden smiling. "What was ordered of me has been done."

The tsar, while watching the quail, missed a step and stumbled down the veranda steps with a crash.

The maiden rushed to help him, as did the tsar's servants. He got up groaning.

The tsarevich heard the commotion and dashed to the porch. When he saw his bride he was overjoyed.

The tsar soon gained control of himself and said:

"Most welcome guest, you have faithfully carried out my instructions. We will now go to my chambers to see the tsarina." But he thought to himself: Nothing can now be changed—a tsar must keep his promise. However, this is not the end.

The maiden hid behind a currant bush, swiftly took off the netting, and dressed in her native costume.

Everyone stared. They could not stop gazing at her as they thought, never has there been a maiden of such beauty.

The tsarina dried her tears when she saw the maiden, for she, too, was impressed by the bride her son had chosen.

The tsar said:

"All three tasks were completed by this maiden. Proceed with the arrangements for the wedding."

After the marriage the young couple lived in perfect harmony in their love and in their understanding of one another.

Some time later the old tsar and his tsarina decided to travel to another country to visit the tsarina's sister. Before they departed, the tsar told the young couple:

"Until I return, my beloved son, you have all the tsar's rights and you must decide as best you can what needs to be done. And you, not your wife, must guard our possessions and keep order in the palace. See to it that others do not interfere, as these matters are not in the realm of a woman. If you do not obey, you can expect to be punished upon my return."

The tsar and tsarina then rode away.

The following day the tsarevich also left the palace to hunt. He met a poor peasant who asked:

"Kind sir, can you tell me how I may see the tsar?"

"But why do you want to see the tsar?" asked the tsarevich.

"Because," replied the peasant, "I want to know whether truth and just laws still exist in our land."

"Why do you think that truth and law may have vanished in our land?" asked the tsarevich.

"I'll tell you why. Because a poor man always seems to be at fault, while a rich man always seems to have the right on his side," the peasant replied.

"How is that?" the astonished tsarevich demanded.

So the peasant told him: "Yesterday it became necessary for me to appear in court against my rich neighbor.

35

From this experience I learned that a rich man is always considered right, and in a court action there is no such thing as truth."

The tsarevich asked the name of the person who appeared against the peasant, and who was the judge. He then said:

"Tomorrow at noon be present at the tsar's palace."

The tsarevich returned home and the judge and the rich peasant were ordered to appear at the palace.

The next day with the judge, the rich peasant and the poor peasant, the tsarevich held court on the veranda. He said to the poor peasant:

"Tell me what you wish of the tsar."

"That the truth in this matter be decided," the poor man answered, and told his side of the story. "My neighbor and I once rode to the bazaar. We harnessed my mare to his wagon. At night it became necessary for us to sleep in a field. The next morning there was a colt under the wagon. My mare had given birth to the foal that also belonged to me."

"No, you lie," cried out the rich peasant. "It was my wagon, so the foal is mine."

The tsarevich addressed the judge: "You are the judge, what was your decision? Who is the true owner of the foal?"

"I decided according to the law. The one who owns the wagon was the rightful owner." And he pointed to the rich peasant. "It is his foal."

"How did you reach this decision?" asked the tsarevich. The judge answered:

"According to the testimony, the foal was first seen

asleep under the wagon—therefore the rightful owner is the wagon and not the mare."

The tsarevich considered the decision. The question in this case was: Why was the foal asleep under the wagon and not near the mare? It would seem that the judge had reached the correct ruling.

At this moment the young wife of the tsarevich stepped up to the veranda.

"The owner of the foal is an easy matter to decide," she said.

"Why do you think it is such an easy matter?" asked the tsarevich.

"For this reason," said the wife; "the foal will run after its owner. You, wagon owner, pull your wagon to the north, and you, owner of the mare, lead her to the south."

They did as she bid. The foal at once ran after the mare.

"You see," said the wise young wife, "the judge was in error."

And the tsarevich ordered the foal to be given to the poor peasant.

The judge was dismissed and replaced by another.

Finally the tsar and tsarevna returned home. The boyars at once complained to the tsar.

"During your absence, tsar, the tsarevich's wife made all the decisions and men of your loyal staff have been dismissed from their duties. The tsarevich has been completely bewitched. He listens to his wife's judgment and ignores the advice of all the boyars."

The old tsar sent for his daughter-in-law.

"You did not obey my orders, and for this you must leave the palace forever."

"Where can I go?" she asked. "How can I live? My dearest possession is here."

The old tsar thought: Precious jewelry and finery is what she is after, and replied:

"Take anything you desire, only leave so we will never see you again. Tomorrow morning you must go."

He then ordered the horses prepared for her departure.

The next day the tsar asked:

"Did the peasant's daughter leave?"

"Yes, she left and took the tsarevich with her," replied a servant.

"What is this? The tsarevich left also?" cried out the tsar.

"She said," answered the servant, "you permitted her to take her most prized possession, and nothing is more precious to her than the tsarevich."

The tsar was deeply disturbed.

"Well! I was thinking only of worldly goods. Have someone ride out and see to it that the tsarevich and his wife return to the palace at once!"

The tsarevich and his wife returned and they lived happily ever after. When the tsar died, his son took his place and the young tsar ruled justly and wisely with the aid of his beautiful, wise tsarina.

A RUPEE EARNED
An Armenian Tale

Once upon a time, in a land to the north, there lived a blacksmith who had worked hard all his life to provide for the needs of his family. So diligently had he labored and so carefully had he saved that his wife and his children never knew want, and he even managed to put by a small store of wealth.

But unlike his father, the son of this industrious man was such a lazybones that in the whole wide world there was none to equal him. Although he was healthy and strong he did not know how to do anything but eat, drink, and sleep in the shade. In all the twenty years of his life he had not earned a single anna, and he never gave a thought to the fact that he was living on his father's bread.

Now the time came when the blacksmith grew old and no longer had the strength to raise a spark from his anvil. Finally the old man took to his bed, and when he realized that death was near, he called his son to his side.

"I do not know why you are so lazy," the aged blacksmith lamented. "You cannot take after me, for I have been on friendly terms with work my whole life long.

Little by little I acquired my household goods by toil and honest sweat. How can it be that a son of mine cannot earn even one rupee?"

"Well, to earn just a rupee is not such a magnificent thing," the youth replied.

"My son," said the father, "show me that you can earn one rupee and all that I own will be yours when I die. Yes, you must prove to me now that you can earn something by the labor of your hands; otherwise, when I am gone you will not receive a rusty horseshoe nail. That is my will."

Now the blacksmith's son wanted very much to come into this inheritance, but he was so lazy he hated to bestir himself to perform the small task his father required. Besides, he did not know how. What a cruel thing, to have to earn a whole rupee when he had never earned a single anna since the day he was born! But a paternal word is a stone mountain, and as a stone mountain is not removed, a paternal word is not changed. His father had spoken.

The doting mother of this good-for-nothing youth could not bear to see him suffer. When she found a convenient moment, she said to him:

"Listen, little son, here is a rupee for you. Go and amuse yourself today, but when you come home in the evening, pretend you are returning from work and tell your father that you have earned the money."

The youth was so lazy he did not want to bother himself even this much, but he knew that something had to be done. So he took his mother's rupee, and with a bit of bread and cheese and a leather bag of wine he went off into the mountains. All day long he ate and drank and counted the birds in the sky. Then at nightfall he returned home and gave his father the rupee, saying:

"Here, Father, take it. It wasn't easy for me to earn this rupee. I cannot straighten my back, I worked so hard."

The father took the coin, looked at it from both sides, and tossed it from palm to palm. Then he threw it into the fire.

"No," he said, "you did not earn that rupee."

With a shrug of his shoulders the son replied: "Well, you don't have to believe me." And he went off to bed.

The next day the worried mother gave her son a second rupee, but this time she instructed him:

"Sleep all day if you wish, little son, but before you come home in the evening, run one mile. You will perspire, you will be tired, and then your father will believe that you have been at work, and that you did his bidding and earned the money by your labor."

The lazybones cared for his legs, but he cared still more to inherit his father's fortune. So he took his mother's rupee, and with food and drink he set out for the mountains as before. From dawn to dusk he ate and drank and warmed himself in the sun, but when it came time to go home he ran a mile, and then for good measure he ran another.

And when he arrived at the threshold he was so tired he could hardly draw a breath. Perspiration poured from him in streams. He toppled onto a bench and held out the rupee.

"It surely was hard for me to earn this rupee!" he

gasped. "I worked like an ox the livelong day. I am falling over my feet with fatigue."

The father took the coin from his son, turned it over again and again in his hand, then threw it into the fire.

"No," he said, "you are deceiving me, my son. This rupee was given to you. It was useless for you to run from the mountains."

What could the lazy youth say? "You don't wish to believe me," he shrugged, smiling. "To be sure, it's not true." And forthwith he lay down by the fire and went to sleep.

The good-for-nothing youth dreamed sweet dreams, but sleep did not come to his dear mother. She realized now that in deceiving her husband they only lost their hard-earned money, and she also knew that all this brought no profit to her son.

So the next day she instructed differently:

"Come now, little son. If you want to inherit your father's property, you must take yourself off and really go to work. If you only earn one or two annas a day, in a week you can make a whole rupee."

It seemed there was nothing else to do; the time had come to obey. The lazybones worked for a whole week. He carried something for one man; he helped with something for another. One man gave him one anna; another gave him two. Bit by bit he accumulated a whole rupee.

Then he went to his father and poured a handful of coins before him. Again the old man turned over the money, weighed it in his hand, and held some pieces up to the light. Then he said:

"No, my son. You have deceived me again. You did not

earn this money." And he seized all the coins and threw them into the fire like so much rubbish.

But this time the son was in a frenzy. He hurled himself into the fireplace, separated the burning coals with his bare hands, and snatched the money out of the very fire itself. "Why did you do that?" he cried. "I haven't straightened up my back for a whole week and you want to burn my money in the fire!"

The father looked at his son and said:

"Now I believe that you earned this rupee yourself. Someone else's money you do not care about—that is cheap. But the money you earn by your own labor—ah, that you make a big fuss over! So it is, my son. Remember my words: As long as you work, you will have money and contentment, and all things will be yours. But if you will not work, another person's money cannot help you, for someone else's rupee is not worth one anna."

Then the father willed all his property to his son and went to the land from which no man ever returns.

STRETCH, PUFF AND BLAZER
A *Russian Tale*

Once there lived an old king whose only child was a son. One day he summoned him and said: "My dear son, you know that the ripe fruits fall to the ground to make space for the next year's fruit to blossom. I, too, have reached an age when I may not see another sunrise. Before I leave for my final place of rest, it would very much please me to know that you have found a good wife. Take yourself a bride, 'my son."

The young prince replied: "Father, I would like to do this but as yet I have found no one suitable and I know not where to search."

The old king then reached into his pocket and pulled out a golden key and gave it to his son.

"Climb to the highest tower of our castle, gaze searchingly at what you see and tell me of your choice."

The prince left at once. He had never been to this tower and did not know what he would find.

He climbed until he came to an iron trapdoor. He unlocked the door with the golden key and entered a huge oval ballroom. The ceiling looked like the sky on a night lit only by glittering stars. The floor was carpeted in green silk. Twelve windows, framed in gold, encircled the room. Each window was made of pure crystal glass which protected the rainbow-colored portraits of twelve maidens. Each wore a crown sparkling with jewels and each wore a wondrous gown more beautiful than any he had ever seen before. The prince could not stop looking at these beautiful maidens. His gaze never wavered, but even so it was difficult to make a choice. All the maidens seemed so alive that it was almost as though they were watching the prince and laughing, although there was complete silence in the room.

Then the prince noticed that *one* of the golden frames was veiled by a thin white-laced curtain. He pushed back the curtain to get a better view and found a maiden wearing a white dress with a silver belt and a crown of pearls on her head. He decided that this was the loveliest maiden of all. However, she seemed pale, sad and lifeless. As if in a dream, the prince stood before the portrait for some time. He stared so long that his heart began to ache. Then he said: "I choose you for my bride and will have no one else."

When he uttered these words the maiden moved her head, blushed like a rose, and in an instant all the pictures vanished from the wall.

The prince came down from the tower, told his father what had happened, and made known his choice. The old king became sad and silent, then replied:

"You have chosen the veiled maiden, but your bold choice puts you in grave danger. That maiden is in the power of a black knight who holds her captive in an iron castle. Many have gone to free her but none has ever returned. Since you have made your selection you must find her, for that is the law. Go now and try your luck, but it will take all your courage and wit to return with your prize."

The prince said good-by to his father, saddled his horse, and set off on the journey to find the princess.

It happened that later, as he rode through a great forest, he lost his way. He made his way through the dense forest, wondering what to do, when suddenly he heard a voice call:

"Hey there! Wait for me."

The young prince turned to see a very tall youth running toward him at full speed.

"Who are you?" asked the prince. "What do you want of me?"

"They call me Stretch. I can be of service to you as I can extend myself to great lengths. Do you see that nest in the tall pine tree? I will bring the nest to you without climbing the tree."

Stretch then proved how correctly he was named for he grew swiftly and soon was taller than the pine tree. He took the nest, returned to his former size, and gave what he had plucked from the tree to the prince.

"You do your task well," the prince assured him. "However, what good is a nest if I can't find my way out of this forest?"

"Well, that is an easy matter," replied Stretch, and again he extended himself until he was twice the size of the tallest pine. He looked in all directions and said:

"We will soon be out of this forest if we travel east."

He returned to his normal size and led the horse by the bridle. In no time at all they were at the edge of the forest. Before them stretched a wide plain but they could

not get there because just ahead was a vast canyon closed off by a high rock cliff.

"Look! There comes my friend," cried out Stretch. Another youth was approaching in the distance. "It would be well to have him with us. He can be of great help."

"Then call out to him so that I can learn if he wishes to be of service."

"He is some distance off," said Stretch. "He probably would not hear me. Indeed, it would also take some time for him to join us because of his huge bulk. It would be better if I went to him."

Stretch immediately extended himself so that his head was above the clouds. He took a few giant steps, lifted his friend up and brought him to the prince.

His friend was indeed a solid lad having the girth of four giant barrels.

"Who are you?" asked the prince. "What can *you* do?"

"They call me Puff, and I can grow very wide."

"All right. Show me."

"Very well, but you must ride off quickly. Hurry, ride into the forest," shouted Puff as he started to inflate himself.

The prince was unconcerned and did not move. Then he saw that Stretch ran full speed into the forest. The prince and his horse quickly galloped after him. He got away in time, otherwise Puff would have crushed the prince and his horse. In the twinkling of an eye, Puff had expanded in all directions and appeared the size of a mountain. When he deflated himself to his former size, the trees at the edge of the forest fell uprooted to the ground.

"You nearly caught me," said the prince. "Yes, one

does not meet with a lad like you every day. You may join us."

The trio continued their journey. When they came near the great cliff they met a man whose eyes were bound with a thick handkerchief.

"This is our third friend," said Stretch. "Take him, too, for he has a special skill."

"Who are you?" asked the prince. "Why are your eyes covered? How can you see where you are going?"

"It is only because I see too well that it becomes necessary for me to bind my eyes. When my eyes are covered I can see as well as anyone. But when I take off the handkerchief I see right through anything. If I happen to stare at an object, it either bursts into flames or breaks into a million pieces. That is why they call me Blazer.

Blazer turned toward the cliff, untied the handkerchief, and stared at the cliff with his penetrating eyes. The cliff shattered and soon there remained only a huge pile of sand. Something glistened brightly in the middle of the pile. Blazer approached the pile, picked up the glowing object and gave it to the prince. It was a solid piece of gold.

"My friend, I can easily see that your help would be priceless," said the prince. "It would take a real fool not to accept your services. Since you have such sharp vision, will you look and tell me how far it is to the iron castle and what is happening there now?"

"If you were traveling alone," replied Blazer, "you would not arrive in a year. But being in our company you will arrive today. They are already preparing supper for us at the castle."

"What is my princess doing?" asked the prince.
Blazer replied:

> "Behind huge iron bars
> In the castle's highest tower is a maid
> That a black knight guards;
> But fear not, we will come to her aid."

The prince said, "Whoever has a good heart will help me free the princess."

They all promised to help and proceeded on their journey. The prince and his men traveled over mountains, through dense forests and hot deserts. If the way was blocked by a barrier, the three friends cleared the path in an instant. When the sun was about to set the prince rode across an iron bridge to the gates of the castle. As they went through the gates, the bridge across the moat was raised and they found themselves prisoners.

Inside the dark somber castle, the courtyard, and the stables were many well-dressed people. However, they were all motionless and looked like statues. The four soon found themselves in the main dining room. The table was set with all sorts of delectable food and drink. They waited and waited, thinking that someone would join them, but no one else came. So they ate and drank their fill.

When they had finished their dinner they looked for a place to sleep. Quite unexpectedly then a door opened and the black knight entered the room holding the hand of a beautiful maiden dressed in white, with a silver belt and a pearl crown on her head. The black knight was ugly and old, he wore a long black cloak, and his gray beard reached to his knees. He had three iron bands around his waist.

The prince at once recognized the princess he had chosen and jumped up to meet her. Before he could speak the black knight announced:

"I know why you have come. You want to take the princess from me. But first, you must watch over her for three nights and see to it that she does not leave you. If she is not with you in the morning you, too, will turn into stone like the others you have just seen."

The black knight departed, leaving the princess behind.

The prince could not take his eyes from the maiden, so beautiful was she. He tried to tell her how he felt about her but she made no reply. She merely smiled and looked at no one. The prince sat down beside her and made up his mind that he would not sleep that night, so that he could prevent her disappearance. Stretch extended himself like a rubber band and twisted along the entire room. Puff sat by the door and expanded himself to seal off the door so that even a mouse could not enter or leave. Blazer stood guard like a post in the center of the room. Soon, however, they were all overcome by sleep.

Just before dawn the prince awoke. He saw that the princess was gone and he felt as though a dagger had pierced his heart. At once he roused his companions to ask what could be done.

"Don't grieve," said Blazer, gazing from the window. "I can see her now. A hundred miles away is a forest. In the center of the forest stands an old oak tree, and on this tree at the very top is an acorn. This acorn is the princess. Have Stretch take me on his shoulders and we will fetch her."

Stretch took Blazer on his shoulders and extended himself to take ten-mile strides. Blazer pointed out the direction.

Anyone else would just have managed to run around the iron castle when Stretch and Blazer returned with the acorn.

"Throw the acorn on the ground," said Stretch.

The prince did so and the acorn turned into the princess.

When the sun rose over the mountain, the door of the room opened and the black knight, a confident smile spread all over his face, entered. Upon seeing the princess he frowned and gnashed his teeth. There was a loud clang as one of his iron bands snapped and rolled across the room. Without a word, he took the princess by the hand and left.

With nothing better to do that day, the prince looked over the castle and grounds, and he was amazed by what he saw. Everywhere all life and activity had stopped suddenly. A prince holding a sword in both hands about to strike was now a figure of stone. Another was frozen in mid-air as he stumbled over the threshold, wearing an expression of great fear. In the kitchen sat a servant holding a piece of meat up to his mouth; he too had been bewitched by the black knight. The castle and all its grounds were silent and lifeless. The trees had no leaves, the lawns had no grass, and the streams no longer flowed. Not a bird sang, no flowers bloomed, and no fish splashed in the streams.

At the end of the day the prince and his companions again waited in their room. Good food and rich wine appeared once more, and again were set out in grand style. When dinner was over the door opened and the black knight brought the princess in for the night. Although the prince and his companions had decided not to sleep, they could not stay awake. When the prince finally awoke the princess was gone. He jumped up and shook Blazer by the shoulders.

"Blazer, wake up! Please see if you can discover where the princess is."

Blazer looked out the window.

"Yes," he said, "I can see her. Two hundred miles away is a mountain range with high cliffs. Buried within these cliffs is a precious diamond. This diamond is the princess. If Stretch takes me there, I will fetch her."

Stretch took Blazer on his shoulders. He extended himself to take twenty-mile strides. Blazer soon stood at the base of a cliff and focused his flaming eyes. The cliff splintered and in the center of the rubble was a glistening diamond. They took the precious stone and returned to the prince. Hardly had the prince dropped the diamond on the floor than the princess was back in the room. And right after that the black knight appeared. When he saw the princess, his eyes flashed with anger. Then *clang!* Another iron band snapped from his waist and rolled across the floor. And he led the princess away.

Another day passed as before. After supper the black knight brought in the princess, stared at her, and said:

"Now we will have the final test as to who will be the winner of this contest."

Saying this, he departed. The prince and his companions tried in vain not to fall asleep. They did not permit themselves to sit for a moment but paced the floor. But this did not help. One after the other they fell asleep and the princess vanished.

The prince was the first to wake just before dawn. He saw at once that the princess was gone and he shook Blazer awake.

"Quick, Blazer, get up," he urged. "Take a look and tell me where the princess is hidden."

Blazer gazed out the window for a long time.

"Alas, sir," he said, "she is far, far away. Three hundred miles from us is a blue sea and in the middle of this sea, at the very bottom, lies an oyster, in this oyster is a golden ring. This ring is the princess. Never fear, we will return her to you. Only today we may also need Puff."

Stretch placed Blazer on one shoulder and Puff on the other. He extended himself and took thirty-mile strides. Soon they were by the blue sea. Blazer showed Stretch where to find the oyster. Stretch extended his hand full length but could not reach the bottom of the sea.

"Just a minute, my friends, I will help you," said Puff. He blew himself to giant size, lay down on the shore, and drank the water.

Soon the water was low enough for Stretch to reach the bottom and pick out the oyster. He took the ring from the oyster, placed his friends on his shoulders and sped toward the castle. However, because Puff was full of water, their rate of travel was very slow. They stopped and left Puff by a long wide valley. Puff spread himself on the ground like a great water tower. He blew out the water and nearly flooded the valley. He just managed to escape from the newly formed lake.

Meanwhile the prince anxiously waited in the castle and he was deeply troubled when his friends did not return. Soon the rays of the morning sun were peeping on the distant mountains and still there was no sign of his companions. As the sun rose it filled the room with light. A cold sweat stood out on the prince's forehead. Just as the sunbeams began to flicker through the east window, the door opened with a crash. On the threshold stood the black knight. He looked in every corner of the room for the princess. He uttered a triumphant laugh but had to stop suddenly, for at that instant the window in the room was shattered, the golden ring fell to the floor and the princess stood before them. Blazer had seen what was taking place in the castle and had told Stretch, who took a last desperate step and threw the ring through the window in the nick of time.

The black knight let out a wild shriek so that the whole castle shook. *Clang!* The third iron band snapped from his waist. The black knight then turned into a black raven and was last seen flying through the open window.

At once the evil spell was lifted and the princess was able to speak. She thanked the prince for freeing her and blushed like a red rose. Meanwhile, everything within and without the castle returned to life again.

The prince who held the sword in his hands slashed at the air with such force that the sword was broken. The man about to stumble over the threshold fell to the ground but got up at once and held his nose in pain. The servant by the stove put the piece of meat to his mouth and ate it. Each person completed what he had started before being turned to stone by the black knight. In the stable the horses stomped in their stalls and neighed happily. All the trees became green as periwinkle. The meadows bloomed with flowers. High in the sky you could hear the song of the skylark, and in the swift-running streams the fish began to splash. Everywhere there was life and joy.

All the people gathered around the prince. They thanked him for freeing them from the spell. The prince answered them:

"Do not thank me. If it were not for my loyal friends Stretch, Puff, and Blazer I, too, would have been a captive of the black knight."

Somewhat later the prince, princess, Stretch and Blazer departed for the home of the prince. They were given a grand farewell. On the way they met Puff.

The old king cried with happiness when his son returned, for he had given up hope of ever seeing his son again. A wedding was soon arranged, more wondrous than anyone could remember. The celebration lasted three weeks and everyone in the kingdom was present.

Some days later Stretch, Puff, and Blazer came to the prince. They told him that they had decided to leave. The prince pleaded with them to stay.

"I will give you your hearts' desire and you need not labor again for the rest of your life."

They told the prince that their work with him was finished and they had no wish to live a useless, idle life. And so they set forth and to this very day they may still be performing needed tasks on this earth.

THE RICH LANDOWNER
AND HIS WORKER
An Armenian Tale

Once there were two brothers who were very poor. They gave much thought as to how they were to live and what work they should do in order to feed their families. Finally they came to a decision. The younger brother would stay home while the elder would take a job with a rich landowner and send his earnings home.

So that is what they did. The elder brother began to work for a rich landowner. He was to be employed until spring when the sound of the cuckoo could be heard. The agreement was most unusual, for the master set up the following terms:

"Should you," he said, "become angry at any time, you will pay me one thousand rubles. If I become angry, I will pay that sum to you."

"But I don't have a thousand rubles. Where will I get them?" the poor man asked.

"Don't worry," his master said. "If you don't have it, you will give me your services free for the next ten years."

At first the man was frightened. The agreement was certainly odd, but he concluded: What could happen?

57

Let him do whatever he wants to, I won't get angry. That's all. If *he* flares up, let him pay up according to our agreement.

"All right," he spoke up. "I agree."

They made their pact and the peasant started on his job.

Very early the next day the owner roused his worker and sent him to the field to reap wheat.

"Go," he ordered. "Reap while there is light. As soon as it gets dark come back here."

The young laborer mowed all day and in the evening returned quite tired.

"No, this won't do," said the master. "I told you to mow while there is light. Even though the sun has set, the moon has come up. Does it shine any worse?"

"What are you talking about?" asked the astonished peasant.

"H'm, are you getting angry?" asked the master.

"No, I am not angry. I am only saying that I am tired and would rest a bit," muttered the frightened laborer, and again took off for the fields.

He started to mow, and he mowed while there was moonlight. When the moon disappeared the sun came up again. The peasant dropped to the ground from exhaustion.

"Devil take your field, your food and your wages," the worker cried out.

Suddenly the master appeared as if he had sprung from the ground.

"Is it possible that you are angry?" asked the master. "If you are, then remember our agreement. Don't tell me later that I didn't follow the rules."

Thus, according to their arrangement, the master insisted on getting the money due him or having free labor for ten years.

The worker found himself between two fires—even to save his life he could not get a thousand rubles to pay his master. And yet to work ten years for such a man was an awful prospect.

He thought and thought, and finally gave his note for one thousand rubles and returned home, depressed and empty-handed.

"Well, how did it go?" asked the young brother.

The elder brother described all that had happened.

"That isn't so bad," comforted the young brother. "Don't grieve. Now you stay home and I will go."

So the young brother outfitted himself, set out, and was hired by the same master.

The rich landowner laid down the same terms—work until the first sign of the cuckoo in the spring. Should the worker become angry he would have to pay one thousand rubles or work for the next ten years without pay. Should the master get angry, he would pay the worker a thousand rubles and from that day each would be free to go wherever he wished.

"No, that is not enough," said the lad. "If you should get angry, you pay me two thousand rubles. Should I get angry then I will pay you two thousand rubles or work twenty years without pay."

"Very well," the master said, with a smirk on his face.

After settling on this arrangement, the young lad began to work for the landowner.

Morning arrived but the worker did not budge from his bed.

The master would enter then leave the room but the worker didn't stir.

"Get up, lad," the master finally said. "It will soon be noon."

"H'm, why, are you angry?" asked the worker, lifting his head.

"No, certainly not," said the frightened master. "I am only asking. Isn't it time to go to the field?"

"Well, so be it. Let us take our time. No need to hurry," said the young man.

At last the worker got up and started to pull on his boots.

Again waiting, the master entered and left the room, and still the worker fumbled with his boots.

"Get a move on, lad!" exclaimed the master.

"Hm, are you perhaps angry?" asked the worker.

"Not at all. I just wanted to say that we will be late for the mowing," answered the master.

"That is all right then. But remember, an agreement is an agreement," reminded the worker.

Eventually the worker pulled on his boots and finally set off for the field, but by then half the day was gone.

"Is it time to mow now?" asked the worker. "Everyone is having lunch. I'll eat now and then get to the job."

After lunch the worker said to himself, "We are hardworking men. It is time for forty winks to strengthen ourselves. Am I not right?"

Curling up comfortably in the grass, he slept until nightfall.

"Listen here, get up! It is dark. Everyone has finished mowing. Only our field hasn't been touched. I would like to break the neck of the one that sent you. May you choke on a fishbone. Go to the devil with your work. Oh, what a mess I am in!" scolded the master on arriving at the field.

Raising his head, the youth asked, "H'm, so you are angry?"

"Of course not!" answered the master. "I am angry because it is dark. Time to go home."

"In that case let's go. Remember the agreement! Woe be to the one who gets angry," reminded the worker.

Returning home, they found guests there. The master sent the worker to slaughter a sheep.

"Which one?" asked the young peasant.

"Whichever comes first," answered the master.

The worker left. Soon the landowner heard voices calling him: "Hurry, your worker has slaughtered your whole flock of sheep!" The master ran out—and indeed, the worker had slaughtered all the sheep.

The rich owner clutched his head and shrieked, "Go to the devil, you fool. What have you done? You have ruined me!"

"You yourself said, 'Slaughter whichever comes first,' and they all came at once. So I slaughtered them all. Is that why you are angry?"

"I am not angry. But I am sorry that so many sheep have been slaughtered," exclaimed the master.

"Very well, since you are not angry, I will continue to serve you," said the worker.

Here the master began to ponder how to rid himself of such a worker. They had made the pact until the first sign of the cuckoo and the winter was just starting. That is a long time to wait.

The master thought and thought, then came to a decision. He brought his wife into the forest, placed her on the stump of a tree, and told her to sing like a cuckoo. Then he returned home and said to the worker, "Let us go to the woods and hunt."

When they reached the woods, the landowner's wife began to sing, "Cuckoo, cuckoo."

"Well. Congratulations," said the master. "The cuckoo has arrived. Our agreement has ended."

The lad guessed what had happened.

"No," he said. "Who ever heard of a cuckoo singing in midwinter? This cuckoo must be shot. Let me see what sort of cuckoo this is."

Saying this, he took aim.

The master let out a piercing cry and flung himself at the peasant.

"Don't shoot, for God's sake! I curse the day we met. What a misfortune I cast on myself!" the master cried.

"Are you really angry?" asked the young brother.

"Yes, yes, fellow! This is enough. Let us go. I will pay the fine and rid myself of you. That was my agreement and I will keep it. It is only now that I understand an old saying, 'Don't dig a hole for another—you might fall in it yourself.'"

The rich landowner learned a lesson. The younger brother tore up his brother's note, received one thousand rubles besides, and returned home.

MOLLA NASREDDIN AND HIS DONKEY
A *Persian Folk Tale*

hree peasants came to market one day to buy donkeys. They found a trader who had seventeen to sell and after they had haggled and bargained until everybody was confused they put their money together and bought the lot. But once they had the donkeys they did not know how to divide them. They puzzled and argued and fought, and finally decided to take the case to a judge.

The judge listened carefully to what they had to say until he learned that, for the seventeen donkeys, the first peasant had paid half the price the trader asked, the second had paid one-third, and the last one-ninth.

The judge thought for a long time and tried his best to solve the problem, but no matter how hard he calculated, he could not find the necessary solution so he could deliver a judgment. Finally he had to give up, and he sent for Molla Nasreddin to come and help him.

Nasreddin mounted his donkey and hurried off to assist the judge. He listened attentively to the complaint of the squabbling peasants and then asked them:

"Well, how do you want to divide the donkeys?"

The peasants answered: "Each of us wants to have as

many donkeys as he paid for, and we want them all to be safe and sound and healthy."

Molla stood up and said to them: "Let's go and see the donkeys."

So everybody including the jury went out into the courtyard where the seventeen donkeys were standing. Molla went off and got his own donkey and added him to the lot.

"Now," he said, "there are eighteen."

"Oh, no, Molla," the peasants said, "we don't need your donkey. There's no reason why you should suffer a loss. Just divide ours so that each of us has those he paid for."

"Molla Nasreddin is not so stupid," answered Molla, laughing. "Be patient a little. You will have your donkeys, but mine will remain with me. The great Allah will see to that. Now let us begin." Then he said to the first peasant:

"You told me that you had paid half of the money the trader asked?"

"Yes," was the reply.

Nasreddin counted off nine donkeys from the eighteen.

"Here is your part."

Then he asked the second peasant:

"And you paid one-third, is that true?"

"Yes."

"Therefore you have a right to six. Is that correct?"

"Well, yes. Perhaps a little more."

Finally Molla addressed the third peasant:

"You paid one-ninth of the price, and that comes to two from the eighteen. Isn't that right?"

"That is absolutely right," replied the third man.

Molla Nasreddin gave him two donkeys, and then mounted his own and rode off.

And the judge stood pondering a long, long time about the wisdom of Molla Nasreddin.

❋   ❋   ❋

When Molla got back to his village it was late at night. He put his donkey in the stable, and, since he was very tired, he went to sleep immediately.

During the night a thief stole Molla's donkey from the unlocked stable, and when Nasreddin woke up the next morning, to his great sorrow he found that his one and only donkey was gone.

His wife and his little boy began to cry, and soon all the neighbors came to see poor Molla. When they learned what had happened, one man said:

"Molla, why didn't you lock the door of your stable? You are guilty yourself. It serves you right that your donkey was stolen."

And another man said: "For heaven's sake, who built the walls of your barnyard so low? Without good walls, thieves can steal everything from you. You should make the walls higher. It was your own fault."

And a third neighbor said:

"Why haven't you a dog? How can a barnyard get along without a dog? You have only yourself to blame."

And a fourth man said:

"Indeed, you sleep too soundly. You heard nothing, you saw nothing, when your big donkey ran out of the stable. Certainly it is your own fault. You should sleep like a man, not like a child."

Molla Nasreddin listened to them, and when they had finished he said:

"Indeed, you are all my good neighbors, and all of you are right. But you should at least have some judgment. What happened was my fault, and in many ways I am to blame. But tell me: the thief, was he not guilty at all?"

Molla's little boy had been listening and he stopped crying. He came up to his father and asked:

"Tell me, Father, did you give water to the donkey last night?"

"No, my son, I did not," replied Molla. "I was too tired."

And while everybody was laughing at this new foolish thing that poor Molla had done, the boy slipped away and ran as fast as an Arabian colt down the road to the well.

Three hours later, when the crowd of men and women were still talking about the stolen beast, Molla's son came riding up on the donkey.

The people in the village were speechless with surprise, and needless to say, Molla and his wife were very happy.

"Tell me, my son," said Molla, "where did you find our donkey? Who stole him? And how did you get him back?"

Then the little boy told his father that when he learned that the donkey had not had water since the day before, he ran to the well behind the village. He saw that the donkey was not there, so he ran as fast as he could to the next well a few miles away from the village over the hills. The donkey was not there, either. Tired and sad, the little boy had sat down and cried.

Suddenly from behind a hill a man appeared riding a donkey—the stolen donkey! The child recognized the animal at once.

As the man approached, the boy began to cry loudly.

"Why are you crying, little boy?" asked the thief. "What is the matter?"

"Why should I not be crying?" the boy answered with tears running down his chin. "I came to get water and I dropped my father's silver jug with its golden chain into the well. My father will give me a good whipping when I get home. What shall I do? What shall I do?

When the thief heard there was a silver jug with a golden chain in the well his eyes gleamed.

"Hold my donkey," he said, "and I will get your jug for you."

Molla's son held the donkey while the thief undressed and put his clothes, his knife, and his purse filled with money on the ground. Then the man went down the well and dived into the water in search of the precious jug.

Quick as a flash the clever little boy mounted the donkey, and with the thief's clothes, knife, and purse ran off as fast as the donkey could travel.

When the boy finished his story, Molla Nasreddin said:

"My son, I bow to you from my heart. Some day, not only our people, but the great khan himself will recognize your wisdom."

THE PEDDLER AND THE MONKEYS
An Indian Tale

Once upon a time a peddler was traveling along the road to town with a pack of bright red caps that he hoped to sell in the market. To advertise his wares, he wore one of the caps on his own head. Coming to a grove of banyan trees, he sat down for a little rest in the shade and placed his pack on the ground beside him.

After a while he became drowsy and stretched himself out on the soft grass. A colony of monkeys were chattering in the grove. The cool breezes blew gently through the tree tops and brought pleasant dreams to the weary traveler. Soon the peddler was snoring peacefully beside his pack of little red caps. And while he dozed, the monkeys in the branches above sat watching him curiously with bright beady eyes.

When the peddler was sound asleep, the monkeys swung down to the ground one by one and began to break open his pack. The red caps tumbled out, and such a scramble you never saw as each monkey snatched one for himself. The peddler had a cap on his head so each

69

monkey put his cap on his head, pulled it tight down over his ears, and raced back up into the trees.

The peddler awoke to a racket of delighted jibber-jabber overhead. He looked up and, to his amazement, there in the trees were the monkeys, swinging gaily from branch to branch, all wearing bright red caps. He reached frantically for his pack. It was empty! They had not left him a single one!

How to catch a monkey? Not just one monkey—a whole colony of monkeys! The peddler did everything he knew to make the monkeys come to him. He called them, he pleaded with them, he threw stones at them, he beat the ground with a stick. The monkeys sat and watched him with their surprised beady eyes—but they kept the caps. In desperation he tried to frighten them by shaking the trees and beating the branches. All to no avail—they would not surrender one cap—not one.

Finally the peddler, beside himself with rage, tore his own cap off his head and screamed at the monkeys.

"Take this one, too, you thieves! Why should I bother to keep one cap?"

He threw his cap on the ground with all his might.

When the monkeys saw the angry man throw his cap on the ground, they all pulled off their caps and screamed and threw them on the ground too.

The peddler stood dumfounded while a shower of red caps rained down on all sides from the green branches. He picked them up as fast as he could and, with a sigh of relief, hurried off to market.

THE GOLDEN DOLLS
A Mongolian Tale

A long, long time ago an Indian maharaja, wishing to test the wisdom of his sovereign, the Great Khan of Mongolia, sent a gift of three golden dolls to his lord. In appearance and dimensions the dolls were exactly alike. Furthermore they all weighed exactly the same, and each doll was made of pure gold. However, the maharaja instructed his envoy to tell the Khan that the dolls were not of equal value: one was supposed to be of very little worth and another only slightly more to be prized, but a third was more precious than a king's ransom. The maharaja respectfully requested his sovereign, in all of his power and wisdom, to tell him which of the dolls had the greatest price and why.

The Khan was very much amused, although rather surprised by the maharaja's strange request. Nevertheless, he called all of his courtiers and advisers and ordered them to find out in what way the dolls were different. The wisest men of the court examined the dolls and tested them in every way they knew, but found nothing to show that there was the slightest difference.

Rumors of the mysterious gift spread abroad, and soon

everybody in the city began to debate and squabble, and old and young proposed the most fantastic solutions. Finally the gossip reached the city prison, where, for a petty theft, a poor but handsome youth languished behind bars.

When this prisoner heard the news he obtained permission to send a message to the Khan saying that, if he could but see the dolls, he would be able, by the grace of Allah, to tell his lord the Khan in what way they were not alike.

"And if it turns out that I am right," he added, "then may I be freed from prison?"

The Khan agreed to the young man's request, on condition that if he failed in the task he had taken upon himself, he would not go back to prison, but would lose his head instead. Then he ordered the young man brought before him in the palace.

The treasurer and the prime minister set the golden dolls before the prisoner.

The young man examined them carefully and observed that each doll had an almost invisible hole drilled in the center of its right ear. Then he asked them to bring him a very thin and flexible piece of wheat straw. This he thrust into the ear of one of the dolls: the end of the straw came out of her mouth. He thrust the straw into the ear of a second doll and the end came out of her other ear. Finally he thrust the straw in the ear of the third doll, and the end disappeared in her stomach.

Thereupon the youth said to his lord the Khan:

"These dolls are like people. The first doll resembles the man who listens to what is said and then tells everybody, friend and foe, all about what he has heard. Such

a babbler is careless and should not be entrusted with any serious matter. His price is indeed very cheap.

"The second doll is like the man who hears what you say with one ear and lets it go right out the other without paying heed. Such a man is thoughtless and frivolous and can never profit by advice. He is not so worthless as the first man, but his price is certainly not very great.

"However, the third doll is like a man who listens carefully and wisely and swallows the words. He hears all but never talks, and for this reason deserves your trust and confidence. You do well to have such a man in your service for he will never betray you, and his silence is worth your ransom."

The Khan listened to the youth with great attention and pondered long on what he had said. Then he smiled with pleasure, and all of his court were happy, and his wife and his beautiful daughter praised the youth. The Khan ordered that on each doll should be written her price and the reason for it, and had them sent back to the maharaja.

The youth was freed from prison as his lord had promised, and not long afterward became the Khan's closest adviser, and eventually succeeded the prime minister.

As for the maharaja, when he received the golden dolls with their inscriptions from his lord, he decided that there was great wisdom in the court of the Khan and that perhaps it would be the course of prudence to serve him faithfully and not start the revolt he had been contemplating.

THE PEASANT AND THE TSAR

A Russian Tale

Once there lived a tsar who enjoyed hearing original folk tales. Soon the storytellers had run out of stories, nor could anyone be found with a new story to please the tsar.

The tsar then proclaimed:

"Whoever tells me a story which I have not heard will marry my daughter and receive half of my kingdom."

Many persons came to try their luck. There were grand dukes, boyars, generals, and merchants, but all failed. As soon as one of them started the tale the tsar shouted:

"Enough! Enough! I have already heard it.'

Thus another would-be bridegroom was turned away.

There also lived in this kingdom a poor peasant. He had neither a home nor wealth of any kind. He lived wherever he could find a place to shelter him. One day he might have a little food, the next day he might be starving.

It happened that the young rugged peasant entered a little eating place in order to get warm. When the people saw him they laughed.

"Did you come here on the chance that you would hear a story you could tell the tsar?" they asked. "Never fear, the princess has been waiting only for you."

75

The young peasant listened in silence to what was said but thought to himself, Why not try my luck? Probably I won't be made a grand duke but I may be given a few good dinners.

He went to the palace and was brought before the tsar.

The tsar asked, "Why did you come, peasant?"

"I came to tell you an original tale. But first, if you please, can I have something to eat and drink?"

The tsar looked at the peasant, laughed, and said to himself:

"What a bridegroom! Look at his tattered shirt, and his shoes are tied with string."

However, the tsar raised no objections.

The peasant was given food and drink. The tsar then called his boyars and grand dukes, and said to the youth:

"Tell us your tale!"

"My departed father," began the peasant, "was the richest man in all the kingdom. He built many great houses. On the roof of three of these houses lived pigeons who pecked at the stars. That was how tall the houses were. The courtyard was so large that a pigeon could not fly from one end to the other in a day. . . ."

The tsar was silent, and so were his boyars. No one stopped the teller of the tale.

The peasant then said:

"My tale will be continued tomorrow."

The next day he resumed the story:

"There was in our pasture a seven-year-old bull. On one of the bull's horns sat a herdsman. Another herdsman sat on the other horn. The herdsmen climbed on the horns and sang songs but neither could see or hear the other. You can imagine how big our bull really was."

The tsar and his counselors remained silent and did not interrupt the peasant. The storyteller again got up and said:

"Tomorrow I will tell you more, but now it is time to eat and rest."

When the peasant left the tsar spoke up:

"What can we do, counselors? I have never heard this story before, but to permit my daughter to marry such a miserable peasant is impossible. You must think of a way to get rid of him.

"Tell him, sire, that you have already heard his tale, and we will all confirm that this story was told before. To make it more convincing, request us to prepare a written record of this and we will all sign the statement."

Everyone agreed to the plan.

As it happened, a servant overhead this conversation and informed the peasant. But the next day, the peasant pretended he knew nothing of this. The story was started in the usual way.

"On the estate of my late father was a mare that could run around the world in three days."

The grand dukes, boyars and the tsar exchanged glances and smiled, but the storyteller continued:

"There was so much gold and silver on my father's estate that our storehouses were filled to the very roof. It was at this time that you borrowed from us a trunkful of gold, my royal tsar. This gold has never been returned. . . ."

At that point the tsar shouted:

"I know it! I know it!"

The grand dukes and boyars chimed in:

"We all know this. A record was made and all of us signed it as witnesses.'

They rushed out and returned with the record.

The peasant took the record, looked it over and said:

"Well now, if you have heard about this and prepared a record concerning the matter, then pay me the debt owing to me from the tsar!"

Only then did the tsar realize that he had been out-smarted by the peasant.

"The peasant has outwitted all of us," he said. "There is nothing to be done now. That which was written by the pen cannot be erased with an ax."

They were ordered to give the peasant a trunkful of gold.

The peasant took the gold and lived happily ever after.

THE HARE AND THE TIGER
A Tale of Afghanistan

There once lived in the forest a mighty tiger. For many years he was an active hunter and was greatly feared by all the animals in the region. However, a time came when the tiger grew old and could no longer roam and hunt in the forest as before.

All the animals were summoned by the tiger, who said:

"I am now old but still have strong claws and teeth. If anyone dares disobey me, it will be fatal. Listen carefully! Each day one of you must come to me so that I can have food."

All the animals were saddened but they agreed. So every morning the tiger had a good meal. There was much grief in the forest. Every day one of their animal friends was eaten.

Now there lived in this forest a certain hare who was much concerned that the animals gave up so easily. The hare decided to teach the tiger a lesson. All the animals were dismayed when the hare told them this.

"What are you up to?" they asked. "You know that tomorrow it is your turn to go to the tiger. It would be better for you to say a prayer before you die."

The hare made no reply but left for his hole in the ground. The next day when the hare was supposed to go to the tiger he did not leave his hole. The tiger was furious. This was the first time he was without food.

The second morning came. The hare prepared to go to the tiger but was not in too great a hurry. When he finally arrived, the tiger asked in great anger:

"You awful creature! Why did you not come yesterday? Because of you I am hungry."

"Oh, most powerful tiger," said the hare, "yesterday when I was hopping over to you I came upon trouble. It so happened that I met another tiger who claimed to be as mighty and great as you. He snatched me and would not release me all day. 'That's all right,' this tiger told me, 'your mangy, dastardly tiger will get along without food.' Only now did I manage to escape him," the hare added.

The tiger was enraged, leaped from his lair and roared:

"Where is this arogant braggart? Show me where to find him."

"Not very far from her, O great one," said the hare. "He lives in a well."

"Lead me there and be quick," roared the tiger. "I will soon take care of him!"

The hare led the way. They came to the well and the hare said:

"He is hiding down in this well."

The tiger looked down into the well and saw another tiger looking up at him with sharp teeth showing. In a frenzy, the tiger dived into the well and drowned.

This was one time that a hare managed to outwit a tiger.

THE MATCH-MAKING OF A MOUSE
A *Japanese Tale*

A pair of mice once settled in a barn and lived happily. They had a sufficient supply of everything—rice, wheat, millet, and beans. The only thing they lacked was children. They prayed to high powers and finally a girl-mouse was born to them. When she grew up, she became a dazzling beauty. In all of Japan there wasn't a more beautiful mouse.

The parents set about seeking a husband. But wait a minute! Could a mate for such a beauty be found among them?

"Our daughter is the most beautiful in all of Japan," concluded the father and the mother. "Therefore, it is necessary to find the best husband for her."

They thought and thought. Who on this earth is the very best, the most powerful? And they decided it must be the Sun, who sits high in the sky and lights up the whole earth. Father and mother took their daughter with them and set off into the sky. They came to the Sun, bowed low, and said:

"O Sun, you are the most powerful. We ask you, take our daughter to be your bride."

The Sun gave them a welcoming smile and answered:

"Thank you for your offer. Only there is another bridegroom who is even more powerful than I."

"More powerful than you?" asked the astonished father. "Who could it be?"

"The Cloud," replied the Sun. "No matter how much I shine, I can't break through the cloud."

"That must be so!" exclaimed the parents.

What was to be done now? The father sent his wife and daughter home while he himself went to the Cloud. He arrived and said:

"Cloud, you are the most powerful on this earth. I beseech you, take my daughter as your bride."

"Thank you for your offer," answered the Cloud. "Only there is a bridegroom on this earth more powerful than I."

"More powerful than you?" asked the astonished father. "Who is it?"

"The Wind," answered the Cloud. "He blows and chases me wherever he wants to."

"Well!" exclaimed the father.

So he set forth for the Wind. He arrived and said:

"O Wind, you are the most powerful in this world. I ask you, take my daughter as your bride."

"Thank you for your offer," answered the Wind. "Only there is another bridegroom who is more powerful than I."

"More powerful than you?" asked the surprised father. "Who is it?"

"The Wall," replied the Wind. "No matter how much I blow, I can't knock it over."

"That must be so!" exclaimed the father.

The father scratched himself behind the ear and quietly went to the Wall.

He arrived and said:

"O Wall, you are the most powerful on this world. I ask you, take my daughter as your bride."

"Thank you for your offer," answered the Wall. "Only there is another bridegroom more powerful than I."

"More powerful than you? asked the amazed father. "Who could it be?"

"Why, any mouse!" replied the Wall. "No matter how sturdy and strong I am, mice can easily gnaw a hole in me. I can't do anything with them."

"That must be so!" exclaimed the father, this time more wonder-struck than ever. He clapped his hands from sheer happiness and said:

"How is it I didn't realize sooner that we are the most powerful creatures on this earth. Well, thank you, Wall."

With a proud look, he returned home.

Not long afterward the parents gave their daughter in marriage to a neighboring mouse. The young mice led an amicable and happy life. They honored their parents and had many children. Thus to this day mice flourish and thrive in the barn.

THE NIGHTINGALE AND THE KHAN
A *Tartar Tale*

Once upon a time there lived a great khan of Tartary. From all the lands of Asia he collected much tribute, and his mighty storehouse was bursting with treasure. His carpets were from Persia, the cloth of his robes was woven in India, he ate from dishes of exquisite porcelain from China.

But what he prized most of all his possessions was a nightingale, who was the very master of masters at singing. The khan so loved this bird that everything that riches could buy was provided for its comfort. The walls of its cage were of interlaced silver wire, the roof was a mosaic of crystal prisms, and the floor was springled with sand of pure gold. Every day, at sunrise, at noon, and again at sunset, a servant would set before the nightingale the finest of seed in an amber dish, and cold sparkling water in a shell of mother-of-pearl. Thus the nightingale lived in its silver cage, and it seemed there was nothing in the world its heart could desire.

"It must surely be," the khan used to say to himself, "that my bird is happier now in the gentle protection of my house than he ever was in the wild forest."

One day the khan decided to go on a journey to a far-away land beyond the mountains. When the nightingale learned of this it spoke these words to its master:

"O khan, you have always been kind to me. Nothing that riches could buy have you ever denied me. Grant me now one request. You are going to visit my native land. There, in a garden by a grove of oak trees lives my brother, who is wise in many ways. Tell him, O khan, that I send greetings. Tell him also that I live in good health in a silver cage and that I lack nothing. Ask him what message he sends me."

This the khan promised to do. When he arrived in the land beyond the mountains he collected tribute from all his people and was given many splendid gifts. When he had completed his official business he went in search of the place where the nightingale's brother lived. He walked and walked, and finally he came to a grove of oak trees. By the grove he found a garden of most uncommon beauty. On all sides there were flowers as far as the eye could see, and pomegranate trees laden with red fruit. The perfumed air quivered with the song of myriad nightingales. On every little branch the gray birds sat and poured forth their silver melodies. One in particular among them trilled out its pearly notes with such skill and fainting sweetness that the khan knew without asking that this was the brother of the singer he had left at home.

"O nightingale," he said as he aproached the tree, "in my house in a faraway land beyond the mountain your brother sings as you do. He has requested me to give you his greetings. He wishes you to know that he lives in good health in a silver cage and lacks nothing that riches can provide. What message do you send him?"

When the nightingale heard these words it made no reply, but dropped like a stone from the tree. In great surprise the khan leaned over the fallen bird and saw it was not breathing. Its wings were outspread, its bill was slightly parted. There was no breath of life in all its little body.

"Alas, I should not have told it these things!" the khan lamented. "But who could have known it would be so grievously jealous of its brother's good fortune! Well," he added after a moment, "this bird is surely dead." Picking up the prostrate form, the khan threw the nightingale beyond the garden wall and sorrowfully left the place.

But the moment the nightingale touched the ground, life returned to its body. Swift as an arow it darted into an oak tree. Then it flew from branch to branch and happily snag its nightingale's song until it disappeared in the grove.

The mighty khan arrived home in a sad and despondent mood, believing still that the bird was dead.

"Well, khan," his nightingale greeted him, "did you give my regards to my brother? Did you bring me news from my country?"

"Yes indeed, I gave your greetings, but alas, I bring you no reply. I fear your brother was jealous of the fine life you live in my house, for the very mention of your silver cage so pained him that he uttered not a word, but dropped from the tree like a stone. When I picked him up his wings were spread apart and his bill was open and there was no breath of life in him. So I threw his body over the garden wall and left the place."

From this moment the nightingale became quiet and pensive. All night long it pondered and thought. The next day it didn't eat, drink, or sing. The following morning, when the servant brought the cold sparking water in the shell of mother-of-pearl and the finest of seed in an amber dish, the nightingale lay in the golden sand of its cage, its little wings spread out and its bill parted. There was no spark of life in the gray bird's body.

In great distress the mighty khan tried to revive the cold little form. He warmed it in the palms of his hands, he stretched it lovingly in the fresh cool grass, and he forced drops of water in the parted bill. But nothing he did was of any avail; the nightingale was surely dead.

Resigned to his loss, the khan sadly threw the dead bird over his garden wall. But no sooner did the nightingale touch the ground than life returned to his body. Swift as an arrow it flew up in a tree. Perched on the topmost branch, it addressed the astonished khan.

"Thank you, O khan, for delivering my wise brother's message. Truly he is learned in many things, for only thus could he tell me how to escape from my silver prison."

Happily singing its nightingale's song, the bird flew away into the depths of the forest.

When the khan heard the nightingale singing in the deep woods he knew that in his house it had never trilled with such skill or sweetness. The silver cage with the crystal roof and the sand of pure gold stayed empty ever after.

THE GOAT
An Armenian Tale

Once upon a time there lived an old man and woman. They had a son who had just married. One day the daughter-in-law was cleaning the rug when she unexpectedly hiccuped loudly. The daughter-in-law was embarrassed. She looked around on all sides. Had anyone heard? Then she saw the goat and was quite ashamed.

"Dear little goat, I will kiss you if only you won't tell my father-in-law."

But the little goat ate his hay and shook his head to the right and to the left, to the right and to the left.

"Take my silver belt, but please keep quiet," implored the young wife, and put her belt on the goat.

But the little goat continued to shake his head to the right and left, to the right and left.

The daughter-in-law took off her silken scarf and put it on the goat. But the goat always shook his head to the right and left, to the right and left.

"Come now, take my necklace."

By this time her mother-in-law came. She saw what was going on and also begged, "Little goat, dear—here is

my shawl—only say nothing to my husband or my son."

But the little goat shook his head to the right and to the left, to the right and to the left.

At twilight the father-in-law returned and saw the goat all adorned.

"What's all this foolishness? What's going on here?" he asked.

"Dear husband," answered the woman, "I will hide it from the Lord, but I won't hide it from you. While cleaning the rug not far away from the goat our daughter-in-law hiccuped loudly. She begged the goat not to tell about it but all in vain. She gave him her belt, her scarf and her necklace but the goat kept on repeating one thing by shaking his head, 'I will tell. I will tell.' "

"Oh," said the old man, "I shall go straightway to the soothsayer and ask if that is a good sign or not."

He went to the soothsayer and said, "Today our daughter-in-law hiccuped while cleaning the rug. Is that good or is that bad?"

"Listen to me. If she hiccuped loudly—EEK—that's good. But if she hiccuped softly—eek—that's bad."

The father-in-law returned to his house, questioned his daughter-in-law, and found out that she had hiccuped loudly—EEK! So he ordered that musicians be sent for, to beat the drums and dance.

The husband of the young girl returned from the field and heard the sound of horns in his garden. He was amazed and questioned the first person he met.

"Tell me, brother, why are they blowing horns in my garden?"

"Is it possible that you haven't heard yet? Your wife hiccuped loudly and the soothsayer said that was a favorable sign. Therefore they are rejoicing and blowing the horns."

The young husband was angry and said to himself, "I would be out of my mind to return to these crazy people." And he set off on the road leading out of the village.

By nightfall he reached a large village. He knocked at the door of a house on the outskirts, and asked to spend the night.

"We beg you to come in. We are glad to have you for a guest," they answered, and admitted him.

In the morning when the hostess got ready to bake bread she sent her eldest daughter for water. The girl went to the spring, sat down under a tree, and noticed that one of the branches slipped down right into the water.

One day I will marry, thought the girl. I will bear a son and I will name him Keekos. He will come to the spring, climb the tree and fall into the water and drown.

And thereupon she began to wail, "Oh, Keekos, my drowned child. Oh Keekos, darling."

The old woman waited and waited for the oldest daughter, could wait no longer, and sent her second daughter after her. The older daughter fell upon her sister and told her about the grief. The second daughter sat down at her sister's side and together they raised a howl about Keekos.

Then the mother sent the youngest, who also stayed to howl over Keekos. Finally the old woman came to the spring herself. All three daughters rushed to meet her in tears and told her about the death of Keekos. And the old woman howled too.

The guest waited a long time and finally also went to the spring. "What is it? What has happened to you? Why are you crying?"

"Why shouldn't we cry, my dear fellow?" said the woman. "Here is my eldest daughter, who will marry, bear a son and name him Keekos. The boy will go to the spring, climb the tree, fall into the water and drown. Oh precious Keekos, our Keekos, Oh Keekos, darling."

"May the house fall down on such fools!" cried the guest. "I ran away from my own simpletons only to meet with new ones. It's better for me to return to my own."

THE PEASANT AND THE BARON
A Russian Tale

A peasant once went to market on a little black mare. On the way he met a baron. The baron rode a beautiful white horse. As they rode along they got into conversation. The baron had a poor opinion of all peasants. He considered them so stupid that he wondered what good they did on this earth. This he conveyed to his traveling companion.

The peasant was hurt and remained silent. Soon night fell and it was necessary to sleep in the forest.

"I will sleep but you must stay awake. You sit and keep watch."

"Why should I?" the baron asked.

"I have a black horse and nobody can see her in the night, whereas you have a white one; a bear will see her at once and eat her up."

But the baron wanted to sleep.

"Come, little peasant, let us exchange horses."

"Well, all right. We will exchange if you wish it."

They exchanged horses and the baron said to himself, "How I have fooled that peasant again." But the peasant curled up and lay down to sleep.

The baron said to him, "What is this, little peasant? Indeed you must not sleep. You have a white horse—and a bear will eat her."

But the peasant answered, "My horse is white, I sleep with one eye and with the other eye I watch, and all the time I can see her. I will not let the bear eat her, You, friend, do not sleep or lie down. Run after your horse. You cannot see her from a distance." And then he snored.

The baron ran and ran after his horse the whole time—and he was soon desperately in need of sleep.

He roused the peasant.

"Listen, little peasant, come now, exchange horses."

"All right, only my horse is better. Pay me in addition three hundred rubles."

There was nothing else to do. The baron wanted to sleep. He could hardly stand—so he paid the peasant an additional two hundred rubles.

When the sun came up they set off toward the bazaar, sold their horses, and started for home on foot. They walked and walked. After a while the baron got tired and said:

"Why don't you carry me on your back, little peasant?"

"All right, sit on my back. But start to sing songs. As long as you sing I will carry you. Then I will sing and you will carry me."

Aha, thought the baron. Here is a dumb peasant. He will sing a short song, but I will begin a long song.

He climbed up on the peasant's back and began to sing. He sang and sang and the peasant went along in silence. Finally the song came to an end and the baron stopped singing.

"Well," said the peasant, "now it is my turn." He climbed on the baron's back and began to sing a song.

"*Tee-lee-lee, da, tee-lee-lee, da.*"

He sang and sang until the baron staggered in his tracks.

"Is that all of your song?" he cried.

"No, friend, it is only the beginning." And again he went on: "*Tee-lee-lee, da, tee-lee-lee, da.*"

The baron was sinking to his knees. "Won't the end of your song come soon, little peasant?"

"No, friend, this is still the middle."

Then he began again. "*Tee-lee-lee, da, tee-lee-lee, da.*"

The baron fell over in the road and cried:

"Oh, little peasant, your *tee-lee-lees* have been my downfall."

"All right then, baron," said the peasant, "don't laugh at peasants. Moreover, your life will be much happier if you stop complaining."

TWO RASCALS
A Kalmuk Tale

Along time ago there lived two rascals, Tzeren from Torgout and Mergen from Derbent. One day they met on the highroad. Tzeren was carrying a sack of shavings on his back and Mergen a sack of camel dung.

"Hello there, Mergen. Where are you going?"

"I am going to your province of Torgout. I have heard that nuts bring high prices there, so I am taking a bag of big nuts to sell. Where are you going, Tzeren?"

"I am going to your Derbent province. I want to sell a sack of sweet raisins for I hear that there the profit is great."

So Tzeren, thinking to deceive Mergen (for he thought that Mergen really had a sack of nuts) said, "Why should we waste time and energy traveling to each other's province? Let us just exchange goods and return home."

"Let us exchange but not look at the goods. Certainly we aren't villains," said Mergen, also planning to deceive Tzeren.

"Of course not. We are honest people."

So they exchanged sacks and each hurried off toward

his own province. On the way they opened the sacks. Alas, in one were only shavings and in the other camel dung. Oh, how angry both rascals were! Each hurled his sack upon the road and turned back.

They jumped at each other like enraged goats when they met.

"Why did you cheat me, dog?"

"Why did you cheat me, pig?"

They yanked each other's hair and scuffled for a long time on the dusty road. Finally they were tired and made peace.

"Let us not quarrel, Mergen. Let us be friends."

"Good. Let us find work together," and off they went to a farm.

"Good day, master. Do you need laborers?"

"I need a handyman and a shepherd," said the farmer.

"Well, why shouldn't we take the jobs?"

So Tzeren became the shepherd and Mergen became the handyman. Tzeren got up early in the morning, took a piece of bread and went out on the steppe. But things went badly for him. The cattle ran away, the sun was sweltering, thirst tormented him, and all day he had to run around on the hot steppe. Tzeren was so tired that he didn't even touch his crust of bread.

Nor was it any easier for Mergen. He did not finish his work until sunset, but one thing comforted him a little. While sweeping the yard he found a kopeck in the dust.

Late in the evening both rascals met near the stove.

"Oh, how good it is to tend the cattle!" said Tzeren. "You lie down in the cool shade and doze. The mistress comes and treats you to tea and cake. You see, I didn't even eat my crust of bread until I came home."

"Yes, but it's also nice to put the yard in order," said Mergen. "You finish your work early. I did mine before dinner and then, having nothing else to do, started to dance. The master was delighted with my dance. He said, 'Good boy!' and gave me some money." Mergen showed the kopeck he found.

"Hm!" said Tzeren. "How about you tending the cattle tomorrow?"

"All right. Then you will stay here and take care of the yard."

Thus the rascals exchanged jobs. The next evening they met with tears in their eyes. The shepherd had lost a bullock and the handyman had not finished his work until late at night. Again they fell upon each other in a rage.

"Why did you say it was nice to take the cattle to pasture?"

"And, of course, you told me that it was nice to clean up the yard."

"But come now, let us make up," said Tzeren. "Why are we deceiving each other? Why not deceive other people instead?"

"All right, then, let us rob the khan's treasury," said Mergen.

"Good. Let us go."

So the rascals took with them a trunk and a rope and started out.

The khan's gold lay in a deep pit. Tzeren got into the trunk and Mergen lowered him to the bottom of the pit with the rope. Tzeren half-filled the trunk with gold and then asked his companion, "Is that enough?"

"Put in more," said Mergen.

After a few minutes, Tzeren signaled to Mergen that the trunk was ready. Then he very quietly climbed into the trunk and closed the lid. Mergen pulled up the rope with all his strength, dragged out the trunk, loaded it on his shoulders, and shouted down into the pit, "Well, good-by, friend. I have the gold and the khan will have your head because you broke into his treasury. Rest in peace, dear friend!"

He hurried off, not suspecting that he was carrying Tzeren on his shoulders. Mergen went on and on until he was tired, then he lowered the trunk to the ground and lay down to sleep. When he had fallen into a deep sleep, Tzeren climbed out, seized the trunk with the gold, and set off at a run. He ran and ran until he was exhausted. Dawn was about to break, and so tired was Tzeren and so dense was the mist that he lost his way.

When Mergen woke up and saw that he had been tricked, he started out after the thief. He ran and ran, then paused and neighed like a horse.

Tired, Tzeren rejoiced when he heard the neighing of a horse, and started softly calling the horse to him, *"Tprocc, tprocc."*

Thus the rascals met in the dense mist, and fought with each other again.

Soon they made up, but when darkness descended, Mergen, rascal that he was, stole the trunk and hastened to his home.

Once there, he cleverly concealed the money, dug himself a hole, climbed into it, and commanded his wife to put a board over it and cover the board with earth.

"Wife," said Mergen, "if a man comes to see me, speak to him thus: 'My husband died yesterday. Look, here is his grave.'"

Tzeren soon came running up and Mergen's wife brought him to her husband's grave.

"Oh, what a pity!" said Tzeren. "We lived together as such great friends. How we suffered and worked together. What grief! He is dead. But wait—this I remember. When we traveled over the world together, we gave each other our word that if one of us should die, the other must pour boiling water over the grave. I must carry out my vow. So he took a bucket of boiling water and poured it over the grave. "Sleep peacefully, dear friend." Whereupon Mergen sprang up like a madman, knocked over the board, jumped out of the hole and seized Tzeren. Then they had a real fight! In fact, the two rascals might really have perished had not a wise man appeared in time to separate them. He then told them: "Stop cheating each other. Live honestly, like brothers, and you both will be happy.

And what do you think? Tzeren and Mergen made up. They stopped cheating and became real friends. And forever afterward they lived happily.

NABOOKIN
An Iranian Tale

O ne day Nabookin cooked a pot of rice and roasted a fat chicken. But as he placed the tasty dish in front of him he thought, "Since I am not very hungry now I could not eat this rice and chicken with any special pleasure. No, it would be better for me to go for a walk and see what is going on in the bazaar. I'll work up a real appetite, so that I can eat with great enjoyment."

So Nabookin left the tray on the table, locked his door, put the key under a stone and went for a walk. As he was walking along the road he met two young men. Looking at them suspiciously, he asked, "Where are you going, you rascals?"

The passers-by stared at him in amazement.

"Ah-ha! You don't answer!" exclaimed Nabookin. "So now I know where you are going. You rogues are going to eat my rice. What do I foresee? There stands my house, and in my room I have left rice and a fat chicken. I have locked the house and put the key under the big stone that lies in front of the door . . . but if you eat my rice and chicken I will drag you before the judge. Take heed: I will drag you before the judge!" And shaking his fist in the air he turned and went on his way.

At first the young people took him for a fool and did not believe him. But passing Nabookin's house they saw a stone in front of the door. One of them, merely out of curiosity, lifted the stone, and what did he see? The key!

They opened the door and there on the table was the tray with the rice and roast chicken. The dish looked so tempting that they could not resist it and fell to eating with gusto, leaving poor Nabookin one well-gnawed carcass. They left then, locking the house and putting the key in its old place under the stone.

After a long walk Nabookin returned home hungry, his mouth watering at the thought of the delicious aroma of rice and roast chicken. Taking the key from under the stone he unhurriedly went into the house and opened the door of his room where he saw on the tray the carcass picked clean.

He began to howl like a savage and stretched out on the floor in grief. Then he got up, sat down near the tray, and thought, "Who ate my rice? If I had not found the key in its place I could say that those boys ate it, but the key lay under the stone so it is impossible to accuse them."

Suddenly he saw a fly buzzing around and then light on the gnawed bones. Nabookin held his breath and, sneaking up to the tray on tiptoe, managed to capture the fly. It tried to escape and started to buzz. Nabookin became furious.

"How can you do this?" he cried. "You ate all my rice and my whole chicken and now you make fun of me by buzzing."

"Zzzzz. . . ."

"A spider's web for you, cursed creature! I must die

of hunger because of you and all you do is just *zzzzz!* I insist on justice. I will drag you before the judge."

Nabookin set off to the judge with the fly in his hand.

"Judge," he said. "I came to you in order to know the law. I left some rice and a roast chicken in my room and went for a walk. I locked the house and put the key under a stone. When I returned, the key was in its place and the door was locked, but in the place of the rice and chicken lay only cleaned bones. I captured this fly at the scene of the crime. It was such a little thing for it to eat the rice and the chicken that it still goes *zzzzz* in my face. Won't you look in the Koran and see what it has to say about such an occurrence?"

Since the judge was bored he was glad of the chance to make fun of this fool. He reached for the Koran.

"In the book of Allah it says that you must let the fly go, and strike it with a stick. If you hit it, that means that it is guilty, but if you miss, that means it is innocent." The judge gave Nabookin a stout stick.

"So it is thus written in the Koran?"

"Indeed," the judge affirmed.

Nabookin freed the fly. The fly buzzed and buzzed and then settled on the judge's forehead. Nabookin swung the stick with all his might. The fly flew up and lighted on the ceiling—and the judge toppled to the floor. On his forehead a huge lump arose.

"Apparently the fly is not guilty," said Nabookin and departed for home.

The judge rubbed his huge bump and groaned, "Oh, Allah, truly one should teach a fool, but to laugh at him is no gain."

SHAYDOOLA

A *Tale of Azerbaijan*

There once lived a lazy man by the name of Shaydoola.

His family was large and there was money only for bread. His unhappy wife and children never had enough food, and indeed never dared to dream of new clothes.

"Use what brain you have," said his wife, "and find yourself some work."

But Shaydoola did not want to work, and waited for help from Allah. This lazy Shaydoola waited a long time for Allah to help him but finally decided to beg for Allah's assistance.

His wife got some bread ready for his journey and sent him on his way.

Shaydoola walked for three days and three nights and then he met a thin miserable wolf on the road.

"Where are you going, good man?" asked the wolf.

"I am going to Allah to beg for help."

"Oh, beg him to help me too!" implored the wolf. "For three whole years I've had a dreadful pain in my stomach, and I have had no rest day or night. May Allah have

106

mercy on me and let me die if it is impossible for me to be cured."

"All right, I will," answered Shaydoola, and went on his way.

Again he walked for three days and three nights and then he saw an apple tree.

"Where are you going, good man?" asked the apple tree.

"I am going to Allah to beg for help."

"Be so good as to beg him to help me too," implored the apple tree. "From the time of my birth I never bore fruit. I toil, I work, I bloom, but every time the flowers fall from me and never bear fruit. May Allah let me die if help is impossible."

"All right, I will," answered Shaydoola, and went on his way.

He continued again for three more days and three more nights and came to a large lake. In this lake a very big fish basked in the sun with its head poking out of the water.

"Where are you going, good man?" the fish asked.

"Oh, I'm going to Allah for help."

"Be so kind as to beg help for me too," implored the fish. "For seven whole years I have suffered from something forever sticking in my throat. May Allah have mercy on me and let me die quickly if relief is impossible."

"All right, I will," answered Shaydoola, and went on his way.

Again Shaydolla walked for three days and three nights.

At last he came to a rose garden. In the middle of the garden stood a big bush all covered with roses of different colors. This bush was flaming with a strange rosy-golden fire which illuminated the whole garden with its mysterious light. Shaydoola stopped dumfounded before the bush, so amazed that he even forgot where he was going and why.

Suddenly a voice came forth from the flame.

"What do you wish, Shaydoola."

"Great Allah, is that you I hear?" exclaimed Shaydoola, terrified.

"What do you wish? Speak up, Shaydoola!" said the voice.

Shaydoola knelt before the bush and recited from the beginning his own request, the wolf's, the apple tree's, and the fish's.

For the third time the voice came forth from the bush. "Listen carefully, Shaydoola. The fish has a precious stone stuck in her throat. When it is taken out it will be cured. Under the apple tree there is buried a jugful of ducats. When the jug is dug up the apple tree will begin to bear fruit. The wolf must devour a lazy, stupid man in order to be relieved of the pain in his stomach. Your request is granted. Be off!"

Shaydoola was very happy. He left the rose garden, his face shining. On his way home he saw the fish. It was waiting for him impatiently and immediately asked, "What happened? Am I to be cured of the pain in my throat?"

"Yes," said Shaydoola, "just remove the precious stone that is in it."

"Good man," begged the fish, "pull out this cursed stone from my throat. I will be cured and you will be rich."

"Oh no—no such work for me. Ask someone else," said Shaydoola, and went on his way.

After three days and three nights he came to the apple tree. Seeing him, the apple tree trembled all over with excitement and was hardly able to whisper, "What news?"

Shaydoola delivered Allah's advice and turned to go on his way.

"Carry out your help to the end, good man," the apple tree implored. "Dig up the jug from under me and in that way you will be rich."

"Why should I bend my back? Why do I need your gold when Allah has promised me help?" said Shaydoola, and went on his way.

Again he walked for three days and three nights and finally met the wolf. The wolf was waiting for him impatiently.

"Tell me quickly what mercy Allah sends me?"

"Oh, it is very easy to help you. You must devour a very lazy and very stupid man, and all your pain will go away."

"Thank you," rejoiced the wolf. "That is really easy to do. Now tell me what happened on your way back from Allah."

Shaydoola told the wolf everything that had happened to him on the way home.

"Oh," snarled the wolf. "Once more I thank you," and leaped upon Shaydoola. The wolf devoured Shaydoola and said, "I swear by Allah you are my medicine, because there is none in the world lazier or more stupid than you."

THE BAT'S CHOICE
A Tale of India

A long time ago a great war flared up between the animal kingdom and the bird kingdom. A bat lurked on the side lines, thinking, As yet no one has declared if I'm an animal or a bird. Some say I'm an animal and others say I'm a bird. It would be best to remain neutral and consider this carefully. I'll wait and see who is victorious. Whichever side wins, that is the one I will join.

The combatant forces of animals and birds went headlong into battle. The bat observed the hostilities from afar. At first it appeared the birds would be victorious. The bat drew nearer to the birds but hesitated before joining them. "I'll wait until they complete their victory before my lot is cast."

Suddenly it appeared to the bat that the animal forces had won the struggle. The bat flew off to the animals and declared, "My face is exactly that of a mouse. My offspring are fed with milk; this is uncommon to birds. It means I must be an animal. Accept me into your family. I will serve you eternally and faithfully. Nothing in the world will induce me to betray you."

The animals believed the bat and accepted it in their clan.

However, the birds vanquished the animals by the strategy of their courageous leader, the eagle. The bat was frightened to death and thought, Should I now run out and display my birdlike claws?

After much thought the bat decided to save itself in flight. It flew to the forested hills and concealed itself in a hollow tree.

To this day the bat is despised. During the day it hides, and only at night, when all the birds rest in their nests, does it fly in the darkness.

KNOWLEDGE AND LUCK
A Czech Tale

It happened that Knowledge and Luck once met
on a narrow path.

"Let me pass," said Luck.

Knowledge was as yet unsure of the customs of the
world and didn't know who should step aside.

"Why should I step aside?" said Knowledge. "You are
no better than I."

It was decided that whoever had the most to offer the
world would be winner.

Luck said, "Do you notice that young man plowing the
field? Join him. If his life is improved through your in-
fluence rather than mine, I shall always step aside for you."

Knowledge agreed and became part of the youth. The
moment the plowman felt Knowledge, he immediately
began to think. "Why should I follow the plow until I die?
I can attain success by much easier means." He stopped
plowing, put away the plow, and went home.

He told his father, "I don't like being a simple peasant.
It would be better if I became a gardener."

The surprised father said, "Have you gone mad, Vanek?"

Later, the father reconsidered and agreed. "Well, be

what you want. God be with you. However, when I die my estate will go to your brother."

Thus Vanek gave up his inheritance. This didn't make him the least sad. He set off to seek out the royal gardener and became his apprentice. The royal gardener volunteered little information but Vanek learned his work quickly. Soon he had little need to consult the gardener who became aware that the lad had a gift for growing things.

"I see that you have more talent at this than I," said the gardener, and let Vanek do as he wished.

Vanek did such wonders with the royal gardens that the tsar was well pleased, and frequently strolled in the garden with the tsarina and their only daughter, the tsarevna. The daughter was exceptionally beautiful. However, at the age of twelve, she had lost the ability to speak. The tsar was deeply grieved and made a royal proclamation: "Whoever makes the tsarevna speak will receive her hand in marriage." Many volunteers appeared; princes, lords, and other nobility. One after another they came and left without succeeding. No one could make the tsarevna speak!

"Why shouldn't I try my luck," Vanek asked himself. "Possibly I might make her speak by indirect questioning."

Without further delay he asked to be presented to the tsar. The tsar and his advisers led the youth to the tsarevna. The tsarevna had a little dog that she loved very much because the dog was so clever, faithful and obedient. Upon entering her chambers, Vanek pretended not to see the tsarevna but turned his attention to the little dog.

"I have heard, little dog, that you are very intelligent

and I come to you for advice. We were three friends, a woodcutter, a tailor, and I. Once we were walking in the woods, and in the evening it became necessary to sleep under the open sky. To keep the wolves from preying upon us, we built a fire and agreed to take turns keeping watch. The first guard was the woodcutter. To busy himself, he took a block of wood and carved a beautiful doll. When the doll was finished, he awoke the tailor to keep watch. The tailor saw the wooden doll and asked, 'And what is this?' 'As you can see,' replied the woodcutter, 'having nothing better to do, I carved a doll. As you will have nothing to do, you can clothe the doll.'

"The tailor took out his scissors, needle and thread, cut out the material, and began to sew. When the dress was finished, he dressed the doll. I was called to stand duty. I also asked, 'What is this thing?' The tailor said, 'The woodcutter had nothing to do so he decided to carve a doll. I had nothing to do so I decided to dress the doll. Since you will have nothing better to do, why don't you teach her to talk?'

"That is just what I did, and by morning the doll was talking. When my friends awoke, each wanted the doll. The woodcutter said, 'I carved her.' The tailor said, 'I dressed her.' I also made my claim. Now tell me, little dog, to whom does this doll belong?"

The dog was silent but the tsarevna spoke instead. "To whom if not to you? What good is the lifeless doll of the woodcutter? What use are the fineries of the tailor? You gave her the most treasured gift—life and speech. By right she is yours."

"You have decided your own fate," said Vanek. "I have

returned your power of speech to you, and given you new life. By right you are mine."

At this point, one of the tsar's counselors said, "His royal highness will lavish great riches upon you for having made the tsarevna talk, but you cannot marry her as you are a commoner."

The tsar added, "You are of low birth. I will give you great wealth but not my daughter."

But Vanek cared little for mere rewards and said, "The tsar promised that he who made the tsarevna talk would be her husband. A tsar's word is law. If the tsar wants his laws to be effective, he, himself, should honor them. The tsar must give the tsarevna's hand to me."

The counselor cried out, "Guards, seize this man. Anyone who says what the tsar should do insults his royal highness and deserves death. Your Majesty, command this villain's head be chopped off."

"Off with his head!" said the tsar.

At once they bound Vanek and led him to his punishment. When they came to the place of execution, Luck stood waiting. Quietly he said to Knowledge, "Look where you have driven this young man. Because of you they will behead him. Step aside!"

As soon as Luck joined Vanek, the sword of the executioner broke at the very hilt. Before another sword could be brought, a runner came dashing from the palace, blowing a trumpet and waving a little white flag. Behind him came the royal carriage—for Vanek.

The tsarevna had convinced her father that Vanek was right. A tsar's word should not be broken. If Vanek was a commoner, it would be simple for the tsar to make him a prince.

"You are right," said the tsar. "Let him be a prince."

At once the royal carriage was sent for Vanek. The counselor who had set the tsar against Vanek was sent to the executioner instead.

Vanek and the tsar's daughter were wed. While driving away from the church, they met Knowledge along the roadside. Seeing that he would have to meet with Luck, Knowledge bowed his head and stepped aside. Ever since, whenever they meet, Knowledge always yields the right of way.

THE SPRING by AY-PETRI
Legend of Crimea

etween Alupka and Mishkor on the banks of a
mountain stream named Khasṭa-Bash, there
lived in ancient times a couple in their declining
years. Their hut was a mess but this was not surprising
as the man was ninety and the woman was eighty. Long
ago their children had scattered and there was no one to
help them. The tiny garden and orchard just barely provided a meager living.

The old man could sense that death was near and one
thought tormented him. How was he to obtain enough
money for a proper burial? He decided to use his last
bit of strength and make a few trips to the mountain
forests for dried firewood. This he would sell at the bazaar
in Alupka to purchase a grave and all things needed for
a funeral.

Early the next morning the old man wrapped a rope
around his waist, took an ax, and leaning heavily on a
dogwood staff started for the mountains. He rested frequently and at length he came to the foot of Ay-Petri
where there were many fallen wind-dried branches.

Having chopped a large bundle of wood and loaded it

on his back, he trudged, grunting and stumbling, down the mountain. It so happened he came upon one of the springs which gives the stream Khasta-Bash its source. By now the sun was at its zenith and the heat and fatigue had completely weakened the old man. He decided to rest. After throwing the wood on the ground, he eagerly gulped the water. Overcome by drowsiness, he curled up against a pine tree and dozed off.

Upon awakening, he was surprised to see the sun descending and the day almost at an end. The old man became very uneasy. He worried about getting home. Lightly tossing the bundle of wood on his shoulders and almost skipping, he quickly descended the mountain.

Then, from habit, he started talking to himself: "You've taken very little wood, old fellow—a very light load indeed. You should have loaded twice the amount."

Meanwhile, the old woman, impatient for her husband's return, decided to seek him in the woods. Seeing a man with a bundle of wood, she turned to him saying, "Son, have you by chance met an old man in the forest?"

"What is wrong with you, Mother?" he replied. "Are you going blind in your old age? Don't you recognize your old man?"

"Don't laugh at an old woman," she said. "You too will be old some day. Seventy years ago my husband was a youth like you."

The old man now realized that he had drunk from the miraculous spring about which his grandfather had once spoken.

He told his wife about the great discovery. She, of course, was impatient to drink from the same waters. He told her where to find the spring and quickly went home. He found that it was many years since the fence around the garden and orchard had been repaired, and the gate lay broken on the ground. Numerous little chores about the house needed skillful hands and a master's attention.

So carried away was he with his work that it was already quite dark before he remembered his wife. He dashed off into the mountains. In a short time he traveled the distance that had taken him many hours that morning. No trace of his wife was to be found by the spring.

He searched for a long time. Disheartened, he thought she never would be found. Then he heard a baby crying in the brush. The dawn was breaking as he picked up the baby to go home. Then much to the old man's amazement he saw that the baby in his arms was wrapped in the ragged clothes of his wife.

It seems that the old woman, possessed by a feminine desire for eternal youth, had drunk much to freely from the miraculous spring by the mountain of Ay-Petri.

A POOR PEASANT AND TWO NOBLES
A Tartar Tale

L ong ago it happened that a poor peasant set off on a long trip with two greedy nobles. They rode and rode until they came to a clearing. They made a fire and cooked porridge for supper. When the porridge was ready they sat down to eat. They put the porridge in a bowl, made a hole in the middle of the porridge and poured melted butter into it.

"Whoever wants to be fair should travel a straight road. This way," said the first noble, and he ran his spoon over the porridge from the hole out. The butter ran out of the hole to his side.

"And I think that it could go this way," said the second noble, and quickly made a path for the butter to his side.

The poor peasant looked at one noble then at the other, smiled, lowered his spoon into the bowl, mixed the butter and porridge and said, "As to my way of thinking, life changes with every new day, and soon will come the time when everything will be mixed up like this."

Thus it was that the nobles did not deprive the peasant of his share of the butter.

The following evening, they again stopped at a clearing.

Among their provisions was a roasted goose. Before falling asleep they decided that in the morning the goose would be given to the one who had the best dream.

So the next morning each described his dream.

"I dreamed," said the first noble, "that I wore a green, ornate cape and a white turban and went to the mosque."

"And I dreamed that I turned into a swan and flew far away," said the second noble.

Next came the poor peasant's turn to describe his dream.

"I saw in my dream," said he, "how one of you was dressed in a green cape and white turban and went to the mosque. I saw how the other turned into a swan and flew away. I became worried, thinking that the roasted goose might spoil, so I took it and ate it all up."

THE WISE DOCTOR
A Russian Tale

Once upon a time a fat man went to a doctor. He began to deplore his weight that brought on other ailments. The doctor looked him over and said:

"Don't spend your money on cures, my friend. You have only forty days to live."

The fat man began to cry. He went home, lay down on his bed, and did not talk to anyone. He even stopped drinking and eating. He thought only about the day of his death. That day seemed to grow nearer because the sick man grew thinner and paler by the hour.

Then came the fortieth day of his illness. That morning the sick man washed himself and awaited his death. But death didn't come. The next day the sick man ran to the doctor.

"You told me that I would die after forty days. I'm still living. Why did you deceive me so cruelly?"

The doctor smiled and said, "Did you not complain about your weight?"

"Yes!"

"Now look at yourself! You are slender as a reed. What else do you want?"

Only then did the fat man understand the cunning wisdom of the doctor.

THE SHREWD PEASANT
A Russian Tale

Once upon a time there lived a poor peasant who had many children, but his wordly goods consisted of a single goose. For a long time he saved this goose but finally hunger caused the peasant to slaughter the goose since there was nothing else to eat. He cooked the goose and put it on the table. Everything would have been fine except that there was no bread or salt. The peasant said to his wife:

"How can we eat the goose without bread or salt? It

would be better for me to take her to the master as a gift. Perhaps he will give us bread."

"It is worth a try, dear husband."

The peasant went to his master.

"I have brought your grace a goose as a present. I am glad to give you everything I have. Don't affront me by refusing, master."

"Thank you, my man, thank you. I will not affront you. Only you must divide the goose equally among my family. You know how to give it—perhaps you know how to divide it. If you can do this, I will give you bread, and if you cannot, I will feed you only birch cereal."

Now this lord had a wife, two sons and two daughters. They were six in all. The peasant took the knife to cut and divide the goose.

"You are the head of the household so the head belongs to you," he told his master. He next cut off the tail and gave it to the mistress.

"You sit at home and look after the house. Here is the tail for you."

He cut off the legs and gave them to the sons.

"And to you the legs to follow in your father's footsteps."

To the daughters he gave the wings.

"You will not live long with your father and mother. You are reared only to fly away. The wings to you. And I," he said, "am a dumb peasant. The trunk is for me to gnaw upon." Thus he took the whole goose for himself.

His master burst out laughing, rewarded the peasant with bread and sent him home.

A prosperous peasant heard of this and was jealous of

126

the poor man. He slaughtered and cooked five fat geese and took them to his master.

"What do you wish, peasant?"

"Here, your grace, are five fat geese I have brought you as a present."

"Thank you, my dear fellow. You know how to give. Let's see if you know how to divide them. If you divide them evenly I will give you money, but if you do not—you shall eat birch cereal."

The peasant tried this way and that, but no, he could not divide them equally. Finally he just stood there scratching his head.

The lord sent for the poor peasant and commanded him to do the dividing. This he did. He took one of the geese and gave it to his master and mistress.

"And now, sir, you are three."

He gave another goose to the two sons.

"And you, young sirs, are now three."

The third goose he gave to the two daughters.

"And you, young ladies, are now three."

And the two remaining geese he took himself.

"Now we are three."

The lord burst into laughter. "Here is a sharp fellow. He divided them equally and did not forget himself."

And the lord gave the poor peasant money, but the prosperous peasant received nothing but laughter.